Radio Receiver Projects You Can Build

Homer L. Davidson

TAB Books
Imprint of McGraw-Hill

New York San Francisco Washington, D.C. Auckland Bogotá
Caracas Lisbon London Madrid Mexico City Milan
Montreal New Delhi San Juan Singapore
Sydney Tokyo Toronto

In memory of our fourteen-year-old
grandson, Justin John Olesen.

pbk   5 6 7 8 9 10 11 12 11 FGR/FGR 9 9 8 7 6
hc   1 2 3 4 5 6 7 8 9 10 FGR/FGR 9 9 8 7 6 5 4 3

Library of Congress Cataloging-in-Publication Data

Davidson, Homer L.
      Radio receiver projects you can build / by Homer L. Davidson.
           p.   cm.
      Includes index
      ISBN 0-8306-4189-0   — ISBN 0-8306-4190-4 (pbk.)
      1. Radio—Receivers and reception—Amateurs' manuals. I. Title.
TK9956.D35 1993
      621.384'18—dc20   93-28869
                                                              CIP

Acquisitions editor: Roland S. Phelps
Editorial team: Pam Reichert, Editor
                  Lori Flaherty, Managing Editor
Production team: Katherine G. Brown, Director
                  Rhonda E. Baker, Coding
                  Jana L. Fisher, Coding
                  Lisa M. Mellott, Coding
                  Brenda M. Plasterer, Coding
                  Wendy L. Small, Layout
                  Kelly S. Christman, Proofreading
                  Lorie L. White, Proofreading
Design team: Jaclyn J. Boone, Designer
                  Brian Allison, Associate Designer
Cover design: Carol Stickles, Allentown, Pa.   EL2
Cover illustration: Homer L. Davidson   4256

Contents

Introduction

BUILDING YOUR OWN BROADCAST OR SHORTWAVE RADIO CAN BE fun and rewarding. Besides learning how to build radios, the book shows you how to make your own PC boards, chassis, and cabinets. You'll also learn how to wind shortwave coils. Constructing a radio receiver from beginning to finish takes a little time, but when you are done the joy and excitement just begins.

Starting with Chapter 1, you'll learn how to build simple radios, using only a few hand tools found around the house or garage. The chapter also tells you how to troubleshoot your radio when it won't perform.

Chapter 2 teaches you how to build six different crystal sets, like the ones Grandpa built in the early 1920's and 1930's. At the end of the chapter, you'll learn how to build a small add-on amplifier so you can use low-impedance headphones to listen to your radios.

Chapter 3 contains five different AM radio projects, starting with a linear integrated radio, then on to an integrated receiver, an antique tube radio, and a radio that uses a speaker.

The real fun begins in Chapter 4, when you learn how to build four different regenerative radios. You will find the antique tube regenerative radio, the integrated tube and IC radio, and the two-tube radio, which uses simple radio tubes that are still available today.

You will enter a new world of radio entertainment when building the five different shortwave receivers in Chapter 5. You'll have fun constructing the one-tube shortwave radio, the amplified-crystal radio with a toroid coil, the 4.5-MHz toroid receiver, the direct-conversion shortwave receiver, and finally the simple superhet three-IC shortwave radio.

Special receiver projects are found in Chapter 6. You will build a varactor-tuning, 15-MHz radio, a one IC, two-band radio, a dual-AM, IC speaker radio, a "throw-away special" receiver, and last, a solar-powered radio.

Several projects in Chapter 7 build equipment to help locate the correct operating frequency of your receiver, to add single side-bands (SSB) to any shortwave receiver, and to convert your camcorder battery to provide power for the various projects. Also included in this chapter is an antique shortwave radio project.

Chapter 8 provides SW radio projects using the TDA7000 IC chip. The first two direct-conversion radios tune the variable frequency oscillator (VFO) using a tuning capacitor and varactor diodes. The last receiver is a superhet radio using varactor diode and toroid coil tuning.

The last chapter shows where to get the parts you'll need for all these projects through mail-order firms. You'll also learn how to make dials, dial pointers, reduction gear assemblies, and you will be shown various connections for the tubes and ICs used in the projects. All tube, IC, transistor and varactor diode base pin connections are shown.

If you can handle a soldering iron and a pair of pliers, you can build the radio projects in this book. Besides having fun, you will learn about basic radio circuits and operations. All it takes is a few hours of working with your hands, and then you can listen to the world.

❖1
Building simple radios

BUILDING SIMPLE RADIOS, FROM CRYSTAL SETS TO SUPERHETERODYNE receivers (or superhets, as they are better known), is lots of fun and increases your radio knowledge and experience. Most of the radio projects in this book are no longer built commercially, but gave a lot of enjoyment in the early days of radio (Fig. 1-1). In addition to learning how to solder parts together, wind your own coils, and listen to stations far away, building your own radio gives a great sense of satisfaction and enjoyment.

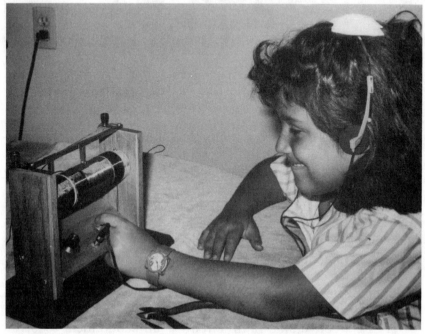

Fig. 1-1 *Youngsters get quite a kick out of helping build a crystal radio.*

Radio circuits

Radios with tubes and semiconductors provide a glimpse of yesterday's receivers. Tubes are almost a thing of the past, although some are still available and work well in integrated radio circuits (Fig. 1-2).

Fig. 1-2 *Low-voltage battery tubes perform well in regenerative shortwave receivers and are still available today.*

Anyone can purchase a commercial radio for only a few dollars, but few can build one from scratch. Building simple radios is clean wholesome fun, a fascinating hobby, and could result in a future consumer electronics career.

Simple radio frequency (RF), tuned RF (TRF), audio, regenerative, direct-conversion, and superhet circuits are found within these pages. The simplest crystal radios combine a tuned RF circuit and crystal detector circuit. The basic tuned RF circuit may consist of two or more tuned RF circuits on AM detector, and an audio amplifier. Most of today's audio circuits are built around a LM386 integrated circuit (IC) (Fig. 1-3).

A direct-conversion radio circuit is an economical receiver. Direct-conversion receivers have an oscillator (beat-frequency

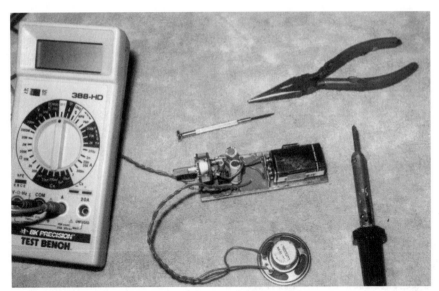

Fig. 1-3 *The low-voltage IC audio amplifiers (LM386) are used in many radio receivers.*

oscillator, or BFO) that operates at the same frequency as the tuned-in signal, thus the difference between the two signals is zero. This allows the intermediate frequency (IF) to provide audio modulation of the incoming carrier. Both continuous wave (CW) and single sideband (SSB) signals can be heard with a direct-conversion radio.

Of course, the superhet circuit provides the greatest shortwave listening pleasure and is found in modern commercial communication receivers (Fig. 1-4). Simple superhet shortwave radios can be constructed with obtainable RF converter and mixer stages found in one integrated circuit (NE-602). A ceramic IF filter can be used instead of a tunable IF transformer. This means no IF alignment is needed. The superhet radio can pick up CW and SSB amateur radio signals with a separate beat-frequency oscillator circuit.

Dollar for dollar, the regenerative radio provides the greatest reception on AM and shortwave bands with the least amount of parts. Only one or two stages are needed for worldwide reception. Its one drawback is that the regenerative radio creates radiated signals which can cause interference to other amateur operators locally. For this reason, these receivers have largely been outmoded with the advent of superhets, but are sometimes used for AM signals. The regenerative radio was very common in the 1930's.

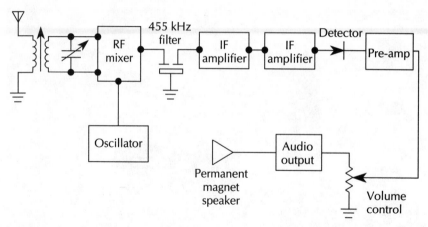

Fig. 1-4 *Block diagram of a superhet receiver with 455-kHz IF filters.*

Pictorial diagrams

One tube and crystal set radios can be constructed by anyone. If you cannot understand or read circuit schematics, you can still build these radios by looking at a pictorial diagram. The pictorial diagram actually shows how the parts are tied together in a picture, while the schematic diagram contains only symbols and lines.

In schematics, lines can cross over and not be connected. Lines connected have a dot showing where each part is connected. Dots found with lines going into the IC circuit have identifying pin numbers. Although the numbers may not be in order around the IC component on the schematic, they are soldered to those pin terminals on the IC or IC DIP socket (Fig. 1-5).

Like the transistor, the base, collector, and emitter terminals must be connected correctly within the circuit. Find pin 1 of the IC and mark it on both top and bottom with a felt pen. This helps you locate terminal 1 when the printed circuit (PC) board or chassis is turned over for soldering. It's best to mount IC components within DIP sockets to prevent heat damage, instead of soldering directly on PC wiring.

Tools

You can build most of these radio circuits with only a screwdriver, wire cutters, and a 30-watt soldering iron. A hacksaw and a small jeweler's screwdriver kit comes in handy with radio construction projects as well. To cut PC boards (PCB), wood chassis, and front panels, use a saber saw or jigsaw. You will also need a

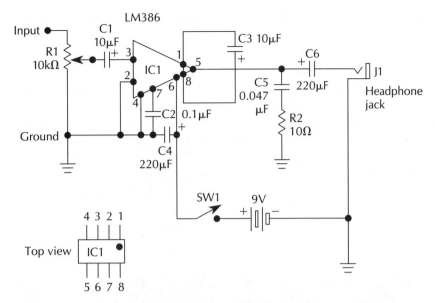

Fig. 1-5 *Be careful when connecting components with crossed lines. If a dot is not present, the lines do not tie or solder together.*

portable drill or drill press to make holes for mounting parts on PC boards and chassis (Fig. 1-6).

To speed construction, a scroll saw, bench sander, and cord-

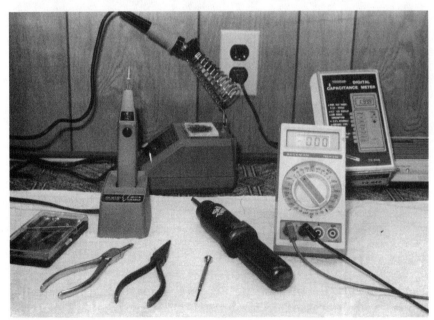

Fig. 1-6 *You can build many radios with a screwdriver, wire cutters, and a 30-watt soldering iron.*

less drill are handy tools. A battery-operated soldering iron or regulated soldering iron is ideal for radio construction. Use small drill bits to drill large holes, such as tube sockets. Large circular saws or punches are not required.

If you do not have a volt/ohmmeter (VOM) or digital multimeter (DMM), select a DMM that has voltage, current, resistance, capacitance, and frequency meters, and diode, and transistor testers all in one meter (Fig. 1-7). Continuity testing of parts and wiring can be made with the low ohm range. Very low voltage readings on transistors and IC components can be made with a DMM. Unknown capacitor values can be determined. Diode and transistor tests can be made with the diode tester. Although a DMM is not required, it can help troubleshoot and find those wiring problems that seem to creep into project building.

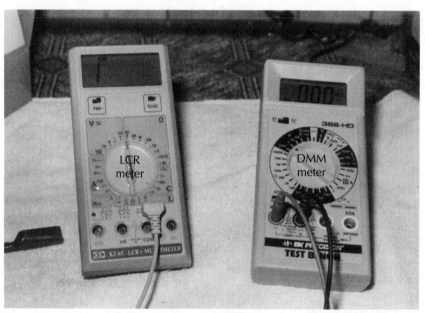

Fig. 1-7 *A DMM is a handy tester to have around, with resistance, voltage, current and capacitance measurements, and a diode and transistor tester.*

Obtaining parts

When building the projects in this book, refer to Chapter 9 for the names and addresses of mail-order parts suppliers. The parts lists for each project often list the names of suppliers that carry the parts.

Variable air capacitors found in broadcast and shortwave receivers might not readily be found at the local electronics store. Tuning capacitors found in radios are difficult to obtain but still available from mail-order firms. Varactor diode tuning can be substituted for air variables, but they do not cover the entire tuning range.

Broadcast variable air capacitors from 365 picofarad (pF) to 500 pF can be ordered from electronic mail-order firms. The shortwave tuning capacitor (50 pF to 140 pF) may be found in surplus markets or mail-order firms (Fig. 1-8).

Fig. 1-8 *The right tuning capacitor may be hard to get, but several are still available from mail-order and surplus stores. Check the variable air capacitance with the DMM's capacitor test.*

When building radio receivers, you can put two or more variable capacitors in parallel to get the required capacitance. For instance, if you have a three-gauged variable capacitor with 100 pF, 200 pF, and 140 pF, you can put all three in parallel and use it for the broadcast band. Likewise, if the shortwave radio calls for a 100-pF or 140-pF tuning capacitor, use only one of the sections in the group of capacitors. Removing stator or rotor plates from old variable capacitors reduces capacity for the shortwave receiver.

Small air-variable capacitors with screwdriver adjustment are easily located on the surplus market. The 50-pF to 200-pF variables are inexpensive and can be converted for set building. Simply attach a ¼-inch shaft to the screwdriver's slotted area (Fig. 1-9).

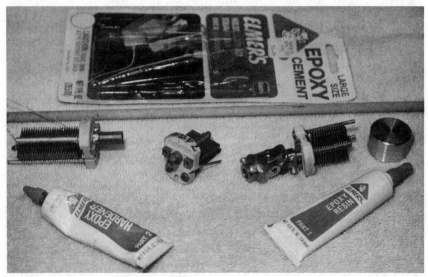

Fig. 1-9 *Low-priced variable air capacitors with screwdriver adjustment have a ¼-inch shaft attached.*

Varactor tuning diodes

Varactor tuning diodes are available at most electronic stores for tuning broadcast and shortwave bands. The variable capacitance diode (varactor) provides a different capacity when a different dc voltage is applied across its terminals. The varactor diode can look like a regular, two-legged transistor (Fig. 1-10).

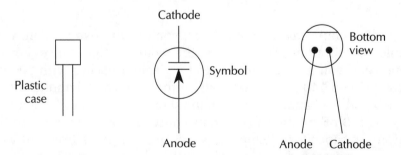

Fig. 1-10 *The varactor diode can be used in AM or shortwave receivers for only a few dollars.*

The varactor diode must have a dc voltage applied to change the capacity in a tuned circuit. When used in an RF or oscillator tuning circuit, a blocking capacitor must be used to prevent the dc voltage from shorting to ground. When different voltages are applied to the diode, different stations are tuned in. Besides regular tuning, band-spread tuning can be accomplished by adding a smaller fine-tuning control in series with the voltage source (Fig. 1-11).

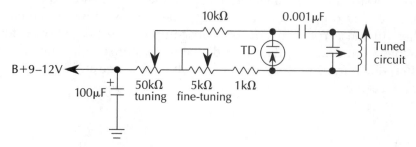

Fig. 1-11 *Dc voltage applied to the varactor tuning diode provides inexpensive tuning.*

The complete varactor diode tuning circuit can be less expensive than the variable air capacitor. These diodes and their corresponding variable resistors and fixed capacitors can be less than $5 while the tuning air capacitor can cost as much as $20. Low-capacity diodes are used in shortwave circuits while larger ones are used in the broadcast band (Table 1-1).

Table 1-1
Varactor diodes listed in picofarads
and range of tuning frequency.

Type (MV)	pF	Range (pF)
2101	7.5	6.1 to 7.5
2103	11	9.0 to 11.0
2104	13.2	10.8 to 13.3
2109	36.3	29.7 to 36.3
2111	42.6	42.3 to 51
1662	275	Goes up to 275 pF

Receiving tubes

Small receiving tubes can be found where antiques are sold and through mail-order firms. Only low-priced tubes are found in the integrated and antique radio receivers in this book. In addition to tubes, the tube socket is almost a thing of the past. These can be ordered from antique and mail-order firms or removed from a discarded tube radio found in the attic or at a swap meet.

Headphones

High-impedance headphones are scarce and quite expensive, although still available. Instead of high-impedance headphones, use a matching output transformer and inexpensive low-impedance headphones. You can purchase low-impedance headphones for about $5 in drug, appliance, and electronic stores. Select an audio step-down transformer with fairly high impedance and an 8- or 16-ohm secondary (Fig. 1-12).

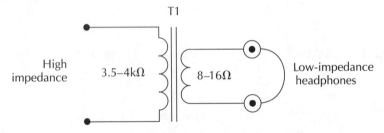

Fig. 1-12 *Low-impedance earphones may be used in a high-impedance circuit by connecting an audio output transformer.*

When you cannot find electronic parts at local stores, try mail-order firms. Some mail-order firms require a minimum order, so if you are going to build several receiver projects, try getting most of the parts from one or two mail-order firms. Ordering parts takes a little time, and sometimes, parts are back-ordered, so look at the parts list of every radio project before ordering or beginning any projects.

Substituting parts

Sometimes you need a certain resistor, capacitor, electrolytic capacitor, or variable capacitor to finish a radio project. When the correct resistor is not available, solder two in series or parallel, then take a resistance measurement using an ohmmeter. Sometimes high megohm resistors must be added in series to get the required resistance.

Capacitors can be put in parallel to get the correct capacity. The project might call for a 0.05-microfarad (μF) capacitor at 15 volts but you find a 0.047 µF at 25 volts. You can use it; it will work. Even a 0.1-µF capacitor will work in audio coupling or by-pass circuits. Always keep the working voltage of any capacitor higher than the voltage of the circuit.

Electrolytic capacitors can be put in parallel with the part list capacitor. For instance, if a 1000-µF capacitor is found in the power supply, you can put a 750-µF and 500-µF capacitor in parallel, as long as the voltage of the capacitor is the same or higher than the circuit (Fig. 1-13). Never install a lower-operating voltage filter capacitor in any circuit.

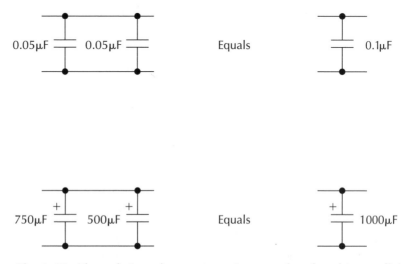

Fig. 1-13 *Electrolytic or bypass capacitors can be placed in parallel for added capacitance. Don't tie up that radio project searching for the right capacitor or resistor.*

The same advice applies to variable air capacitors. If you need a 140-pF capacitor and you have a dual 100-pF and 50-pF capacitor, just put them in parallel and tie the two stators together. The rotors are already tied together. With older tuning capacitors, you can remove rotor or stator plates, whichever is the easiest, to cut the capacitance for a shortwave tuning circuit. However, you should have a capacitor tester (DMM) to measure the total capacitance with the plates meshed.

Winding your own coils

Winding your own coils can be fun and rewarding. Sometimes you have to use the cut-and-try method if a certain coil does not cover a particular band of frequencies. The broadcast band 40- to

80-meter coils can be close wound, while shortwave coils have fewer turns and spread apart.

The different bands

Different size coils are needed to receive different frequency bands. Table 1-2 lists the different frequency bands you will be using for the radio projects in this book.

Table 1-2
The frequency bands.

Band	Frequencies (kHz)
Broadcast or medium wave (mw)	540–1600
International	5800–26,000
Tropical stations	2300–5000
Amateur radio operators (also known as hams)	1800–29,700
Continuous wave (some hams also use these frequencies)	3500–3800 7000–7150 14,000–14,200 21,000–21,250 28,000–28,500
Single sidebands (SSB) (most hams use these bands)	3800–4000 7150–7300 14,200–14,350 21,250–21,450 28,500–29,700

When picked up on a shortwave receiver without sideband reception, ham operators sound like they have mush in their mouths. A SSB voice can be cleared up with a beat-frequency oscillator (BFO) on superhet receivers.

Broadcast coils

Broadcast band coils can be wound on air core coil forms. You can wind a MW coil on a plastic 35-mm film container, cardboard tube, plastic PVC pipe, or plumbing fixtures. A longer coil form is needed for the broadcast band (Fig. 1-14).

For greater selectivity and sensitivity, wind the broadcast coil on a ferrite rod or toroid coil form. These iron-core forms have higher Q and bring in weak stations (Fig. 1-15). If a local broadcast station at 540 kHz will not come in with a 365-picofarad (pF)

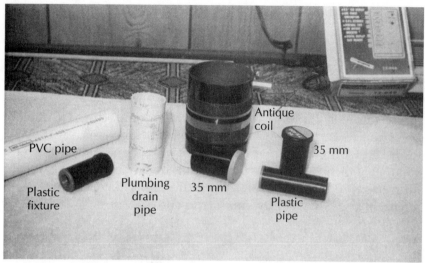

Fig. 1-14 *Coils can be wound on pieces of plumbing fixtures, plastic PVC pipe, cardboard forms, and 35-mm film containers.*

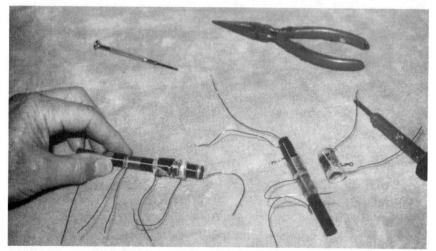

Fig. 1-15 *Coils wound on ferrite or iron core forms have a higher Q, resulting in higher gain and selectivity.*

variable capacitor, add more turns. When a local station at 1400 kHz comes in with the variable capacitor meshed half way, remove a few turns from the coil.

Shortwave coils

Early shortwave coils found in regenerative receivers were wound on plastic, plug-in coil forms. Coil windings at higher frequencies use less turns and larger wire, and are spread over a larger area. Each winding is further apart at higher frequencies. The shortwave turns can be spread apart for higher frequencies and closer together for lower frequencies.

You might find the shortwave coils wound on a ferrite or toroid form. At lower frequencies, more turns are needed with larger toroid coils (Fig. 1-16). Shortwave coils in the 5- to 15-MHz band can have fewer turns over a wider area. A 15-MHz toroid coils might have only 22 turns of #24 enamel wire over a small 0.500-inch diameter form. For instance, a T-50-2 toroid form has an outside diameter of a half inch. This means a shorter length of wire over a very small iron core.

Fig. 1-16 *Round ferrite or powdered iron toroid coil forms provide high gain in a small space.*

Shielded shortwave RF and oscillator coils are found in small and miniature shielded components. You can wind your own shortwave coils with center tunable adjustments on these forms. Select the frequency range with either ferrite or carbonyl magnetic material. The coil should be wound so the slug is set at 90 percent of maximum inductance at its operating frequency (Fig. 1-17).

These shielded coils should be selected to cover 1.0 to 10.0 meters, 9.0 to 40.0 meters, and 30.0 to 80.0 meters. The tunable shielded coils come in subminiature, miniature, and standard sizes. The shielded coil forms can be ordered from Amidon Associates, Digi-Key Corporation, and Ocean State Electronics. You will find a variety of medium wave (mw) and shortwave (sw) coils found in the various receiver projects in this book.

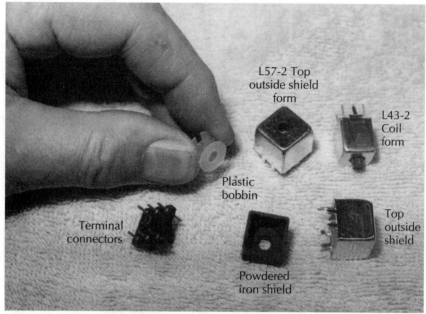

L57-2 Top outside shield form

L43-2 Coil form

Plastic bobbin

Top outside shield

Terminal connectors

Powdered iron shield

Fig. 1-17 *Small shielded coil forms are ideal for winding your own coils to be used in direct-conversion and superhet radios.*

Different sizes of magnet wire for coils winding can be obtained from just about any electronics store. Radio Shack has a 22-, 26-, and 30-gauge enameled wire assortment (278-1345). You can take various sizes of magnet wire from discarded dc model motors, field coils, dc speaker magnet windings, and large choke coils and old power transformers. Check discarded door bells for available magnet wire.

PC boards or perfboards

Radio or electronic projects can be built on printed circuit (PC) boards or perfboards (Perf), predrilled boards, universal index boards, multipurpose or dual mini-boards, and etched PC boards (Fig. 1-18). The perfboard has small holes drilled in a fiber board without any PC wiring. Small boards can be cut from a larger piece. Here, hookup wire must be used on the underside of the board to tie the parts together.

Predrilled, universal, and multipurpose boards have short PC wiring or solder-ringed holes on the bottom side (Fig. 1-19). The ringed holes and pieces of PC wiring can be connected together with bare or insulated hookup wire. These boards are handy and make it quick to mount small radio circuits and components.

Fig. 1-18 *Perfboard material is easy to cut and to mount parts on without any PC wiring.*

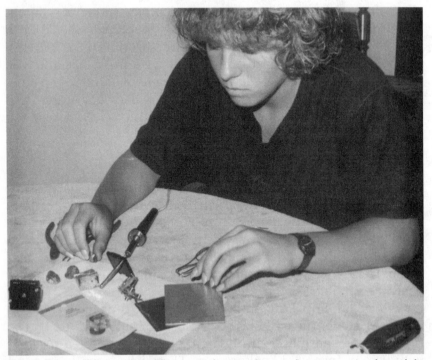

Fig. 1-19 *A PC board chassis may be cut from a larger copper board for etched PC wiring.*

Not only does the etched PC board look nice, but you can mount all parts on it and it's fun to design your own circuits. All RF and oscillator circuits can be mounted close together to prevent tuning and circuit loss. With small radios, batteries, variable capacitors, and audio transformers can be mounted right on the etched board (Fig. 1-20).

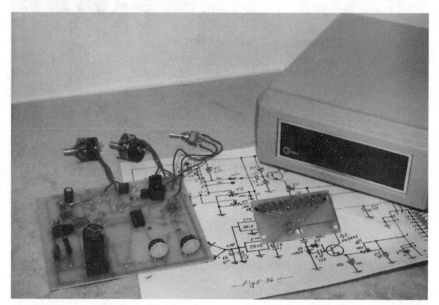

Fig. 1-20   *A professional-looking PC board makes a neat chassis for any radio or electronic project.*

A PC board kit might cost less than $10 and can be used for many etched circuits. The kit might include circuit boards, etching solution, tank, etching pen, ¹⁄₁₆-inch drill, stripping solution, circles, pads, and all material needed to produce professional printed circuits. Instructions on how to lay out circuits and etch the board are also given (Fig. 1-21).

When laying out PC wiring and placing stick-on sheets on a copper board, place a piece of paper on underneath areas so the dots and press-on wiring do not accidentally stick to present wiring. Double-sided boards take a little longer to etch. If PC boards (PCB) are left in the etching solution too long, ragged edges can appear on the copper wiring or thin lines can be etched away entirely. Check the board every 15 minutes.

After the board is cleaned off, inspect the wiring for possible damage. Make sure all circuits and component wiring ties together. Look to see if small wiring is cracked or etched out. Dou-

Fig. 1-21   *A low-priced PC board kit gets you started in making your own PC wiring circuits.*

ble check wiring continuity with the low-ohm range of an ohmmeter.

Antenna requirements

All long-distance receiving radios, even large commercial receivers, should have some type of antenna. A good antenna and ground is required for crystal sets, one or two transistor and IC radios. The high antenna helps pick up overseas broadcasters on the shortwave radio.

Just install the inverted L antenna as high and long as possible. A sw antenna kit with 75 feet of antenna wire, 50 feet of insulated lead-in wire, window feed-through, and insulators can be purchased at Radio Shack for about $8. Back in the old days, Grandpa had enough money to purchase 100 feet of antenna wire, but nothing to go along with it. For an insulator, he broke the neck off a heavy medicine bottle . . . sometimes you improvise!

Install the simple antenna high from a tree or pole at least 20 to 30 feet in the air. Do not place antenna wires near power lines or over them. For crystal sets, the longer the antenna, the greater the pulling power (Fig. 1-22).

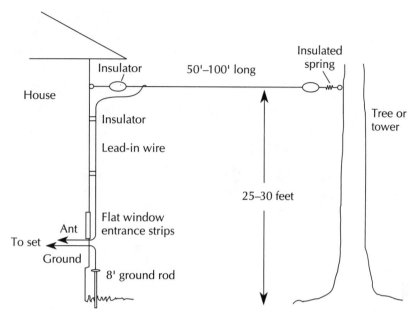

Fig. 1-22   *A low-priced antenna kit with 50 or 75 feet of antenna wire brings in those desired shortwave stations on the smallest radio.*

Connect the ground to a water pipe or drive an 8-foot ground stake into the ground. Place the ground under the window or wherever the antenna lead-in comes in the house. Clean off or scrape off the water pipe and clamp the ground wire to it. Do not use a gas pipe for a ground. Notice if the water meter has a copper wire clamped around the pipes on both sides of the meter. If so, solder the ground wire to the large bare copper shunt wire.

Headphone or speaker operation

Unless you have your own room or are insulated away from other people, use headphones instead of speakers on shortwave receivers. Regenerative radios are quite noisy. Headphone reception is best for any shortwave receiver. Some of the small radios might not drive a small speaker, but can listen to them with headphones (Fig. 1-23).

High-impedance headphones (2000 ohms) are quite expensive when compared to the low-impedance ones (8 to 32 ohms). They are still available at antique electronic mail-order stores. The low-impedance headphones can be found for $5 to $20 most anywhere.

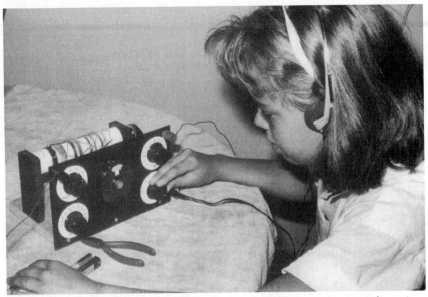

Fig. 1-23 *Headphone operation is best for shortwave and private listening.*

Many of the radio receivers found in this book have enough volume to drive a small permanent magnet (PM) speaker. In fact, some of the projects do have speaker operation. The 8-ohm PM speaker can be added to radios with sufficient audio and switched in and out of the circuit with a headphone self-shorted jack. With this arrangement, headphones can be used when needed for quiet listening.

Bandspread tuning

When building shortwave radios, you'll find stations are bunched together; they fade in and out, and they are hard to separate. Bandspread tuning helps to separate hams from worldwide broadcast programs. Stations can be separated using mechanical tuning by slowing down the rotation of the main variable tuning capacitor. To do this, we use built-in 6:1 or 7:1 shaft reduction assemblies and vernier dial drive assemblies (Fig. 1-24). If you cannot afford any of these, select the largest knob dial so the capacitor rotates slower.

Electronic bandspreading can also be accomplished by adding a smaller variable air capacitor in parallel with the main tuning capacitor. Locate the correct stations with the main tuning capacitor and separate them with the small capacitor. Usually, 10-pF to 35-pF

Fig. 1-24 *The vernier dial on this receiver provides slow bandspread tuning.*

variable capacitors are used for bandspreading the stations. Go a step farther and place the bandspread capacitor on a reduction gear or vernier dial drive assembly.

You can electronically add a small varactor tuning diode to the circuit to provide electronic bandspreading. Take a MV2104 (13.2 pF) or MV2109 (36.3 pF) and add it in parallel with the main tuning capacitor. Just use a variable resistor in place of the air variable capacitor (Fig. 1-25). Of course, dc voltage must be applied to the varactor diode. You can save a few dollars with this varactor diode bandspread application.

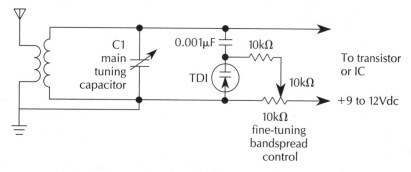

Fig. 1-25 *Bandspread tuning can be done with a small varactor tuning diode and variable resistance.*

Cabinet and chassis construction

You can build your own cabinets and chassis out of scrap pieces of wood. Clean pine or ash make an ideal rear chassis with plastic, phenlic, or masonite front panels. The L chassis was used extensively in Grandpa's days and can still be used today. Shortwave circuits, including antenna posts, should be insulated from the pieces of wood.

PC boards are used today for the main chassis and can be slipped into commercial cabinets (Fig. 1-26). You can use the PC as both chassis and front panel. Simply mount the components as surface-mounted components behind the front panel. Several radio projects within these pages use this method.

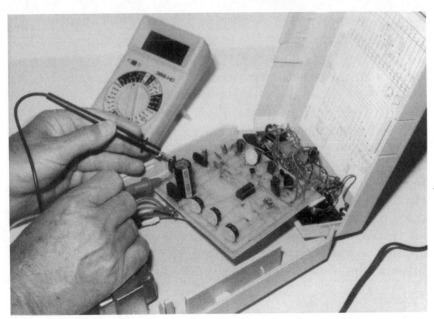

Fig. 1-26 *Place the radio circuit on a PC board and mount it in a commercial or surplus plastic or metal chassis.*

By choosing the right cabinet or enclosure, you can dress up the radio project. Most electronic stores sell attractive plastic or metal cabinets. Also, you can pick up nice looking surplus cabinets and test instrument cabinets from $1 to $5.

Always lay out the front panel on a clean sheet of paper before mounting any parts. Try to balance the mounting holes. Use transparent tape to secure the paper to the front panel to prevent scratching and marring. Remove the layout paper after all holes are drilled.

Clean off the front panel with soap and water. Dress up the front panel with press-on labels and letters. Rub-on transfer lettering and dial drawings can be purchased at most local electronic stores. Custom dial plates, switch patterns, and variable capacitor settings are available from Digi-Key Corp. (the address is listed in Chapter 9). Keep all numbers and label lettering square and level with the front panel (Fig. 1-27). Spray on a clear coat of acrylic or lacquer over the entire front panel for a professional finish.

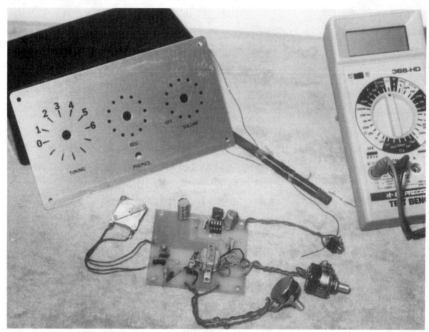

Fig. 1-27 *Before mounting any parts, letter and mark all front dial settings with rub-on transfer decals. Spray on a coat of clear acrylic or lacquer finish for protection.*

Last, apply plastic rubber feet to the finished radio project. Usually, screws, bolts, or nuts are found under the chassis for mounting larger components. The radio will not set level if feet are not added. Select screw hole wood plugs to glue as feet on the wood rear chassis or cabinet (Fig. 1-28).

Battery or ac operation

Small flashlight and 9-volt batteries power many of the radio projects. They are easily obtained and can be mounted in regular

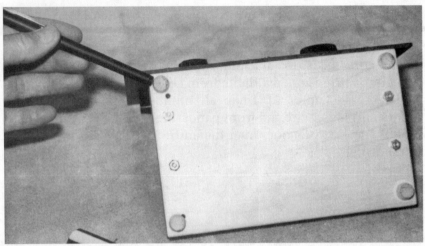

Fig. 1-28 *Dress up the finished radio project with rubber, plastic or wooden feet.*

plastic holders. Like the transistor, diode, or electrolytic capacitor, observe correct polarity. Even tube or integrated radio circuits can be powered with batteries wired in series.

Of course, batteries only last so long and must be replaced. Battery replacement can be expensive. If you plan on building several radio or electronic projects operated by batteries, you might want to purchase rechargeable batteries. Nickel-cadmium batteries can be recharged and last for years.

Today, nickel-cadmium batteries are fairly inexpensive compared to a few years ago. You can purchase a battery charger to fit any budget (Fig. 1-29). In fact, you can purchase a deluxe D, C, AA, AAA, N, and 9-volt battery charger all in one for less than $25.

The ac power supply must be built to change low ac to dc voltage. Several of the radio projects in the book are ac operated. Be careful when working around a 120-volt power line. Make sure all ac wires and switch connections are covered with tape, insulation, or rubber silicone cement. In radio projects, instead of switching the ac power line, wire the connection directly to the secondary of the step-down transformer and switch the low-voltage secondary source. Many commercial compact disc, cassette players, and radios use this method (Fig. 1-30). Remember, accidentally touching the hot side of a power line can cause serious shock, injury, or death.

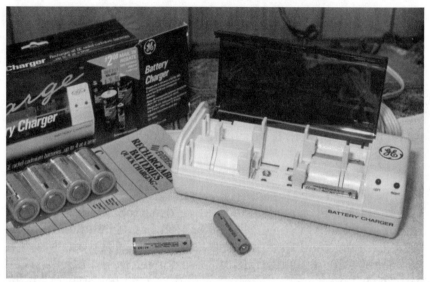

Fig. 1-29   *If you build a lot of radio and electronic projects that are operated from batteries, purchase nickel-cadmium rechargeable batteries.*

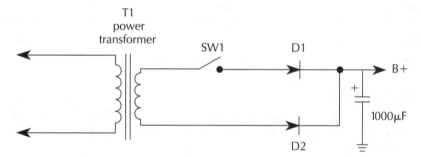

Fig. 1-30   *When building radios or electronic projects operating on an ac power line, switch the secondary instead of the primary winding of the power transformer.*

Construction hints

Here are some radio and electronic construction hints that you might want to follow in constructing the 33 radio projects:

Soldering

When soldering wires together near wood rear chassis or front panels, place a piece of paper or cardboard between wires and board to prevent burn or solder marks.

Look for poorly soldered joints on the PC board or wiring before trying out the radio project. Check the IC socket connection from the top of the socket to the first connected wiring component. Look for poorly etched PC wiring.

When using shielded cable between antenna and tuned circuits or in audio circuits, check for a possible short between the center cable and shield with the low range of an ohmmeter. If too much heat is applied, the insulation breaks down between shield and center wire.

Etching boards

When placing PC transfers to the board wiring layout, place paper or an insulated sheet over areas that have been done to prevent extra dots and lines from sticking to the PC layout.

Double-sided boards take a little longer to etch both sides. Turn board over every 15 minutes and take a peek. Warm up the etching solution in a pan of warm water to speed up the etching process. Keep etching solution away from hands, eyes, and tender skin areas.

When the board is finished and cleaned up, check the thin wiring lines for continuity with the low ohm range of an ohmmeter. Patch broken wiring with pieces of bare hookup wire.

Winding coils

When winding coils, the small copper wire tends to kink up. Unwind the kink and run the wire between thumb and wooden pencil to easily remove the kinked wire.

When winding toroid coils, cut off a shorter piece of wire. Usually 24 inches of wire will wind most toroid coils. Place thumb along hole to hold winding in position. Push wire through hole and pull excess through. Check for kinked wiring.

When winding close-wound coils, be careful not to place one winding of wire over another one. Just place each winding next to the previous one.

Tapped coils can easily be made while holding the coil wire taut and twisting a loop six or eight times. Keep taps in line. After coil is completely wound, twist each tap several times to tighten the wire and any excess coil wire. Solder tap and cut off excess wire.

Remove the enamel from the bare copper wire before soldering a connection. Scrape excess enamel off with a pocketknife or other tool and tin with solder. You can remove excess enamel from copper wire without scraping using heat from a high-wattage soldering gun (150 to 250 watts).

Front panels

Lay out front panel on a piece of paper or cardboard. Tape the paper to the front panel for drilling. Use a punch to mark each center hole to prevent the drill from skidding and marring the front panel.

Mounting parts

Variable capacitors can be mounted at the front or bottom area of the capacitor. To position the capacitor over the dial hole for mounting, place a sheet of paper at the edge of the capacitor and push holes through with a pencil point. Lay paper on the area to be mounted and mark the pencil holes. Double check the holes to be drilled.

You may have to cut off small bolts to mount the variable capacitor at the front or bottom mounting area. Cut or grind off bolts to just go through the front panel and metal base of the capacitor. If the bolts are too long at the bottom mounting, the stator plates can be thrown out of line and might damage an expensive variable capacitor.

Variable resistance controls, headphone jacks, antenna and ground jacks, and mounting bolts can be held in position by placing a coat of paint or fingernail polish over the area so it cannot be rotated or loosened.

Cutting small bolts

To cut off small mounting bolts to mount variable capacitors or brackets, place the nut over the bolt to be cut. Put the bolt in a bench vise and cut off with a hacksaw. If an electric grinder or sander is handy, hold the nut with a large pair of pliers and touch the bolt end to be removed on the grinder area. The bolt and nut can become hot so exercise caution.

Safety

Always exercise safety around power lines and when working with power tools. Do not touch metal ducts, metal posts, or grounded metal while drilling. Periodically inspect ac drills, soldering irons, and cords for frayed or worn power cords. Watch where you place that hot soldering iron. Practicing good safety procedures can prevent any serious injury.

Troubleshooting

Double check and check again all wiring connections, part connections, and connecting wires before trying out the radio project. Make sure the transistor or IC component is wired or mounted in the socket correctly. Check the polarity of electrolytic capacitors, diodes, and batteries. Check the wiring between components with the low ohm range of an ohmmeter.

The great moment has arrived when the radio project is finished and ready for a test. Sometimes you can't wait to try it out! It's a great pleasure when the radio performs the first time. But, it's also very discouraging when a homebuilt electronic project does not work. So, check and double check to make it work the first time!

Take resistance and voltage measurements on the transistor and IC terminals and compare these voltages to those found on the schematic. Take a complete current test of the whole radio by placing the milliampere meter probes between battery and switch. A quick test is to place the meter probes across the bare switch terminals with the switch turned off (Fig. 1-31).

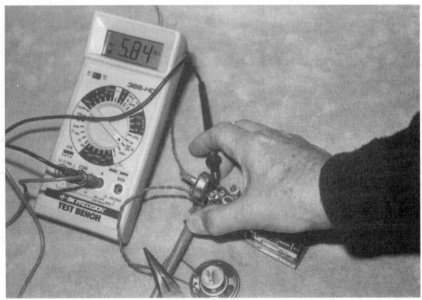

Fig. 1-31 *If the circuit is suspected of drawing excessive current, measure the total current across the ON/OFF switch terminals with the switch turned OFF.*

Don't forget it is possible to purchase a defective transistor or IC components. Test transistors out with a beta transistor tester or diode tester located on the portable digital multimeter (DMM). Check continuity of resistors, PC wiring, and transformers. Make sure all prongs of the small IC are in the socket. Sometimes, one slips out alongside and prevents the radio from functioning. Too much heat applied to transistors, ICs, varactor diodes, and signal diode terminals can damage the component.

Above all, be careful and safe. Now, let's build a few receivers and begin to have some fun, fun, fun!

❖2
Crystal radio projects

CRYSTAL SETS ARE EASY AND INEXPENSIVE TO BUILD. THIS CHAPTER contains five crystal radio projects, plus an IC audio amplifier project. It's fun to construct a radio with your own hands. A piece of pencil lead, razor blade, and coil were used in the trenches of World War I. They have been around since Grandpa was a kid. Building a crystal radio sparked many people's interest in electronics.

You can put that crystal set together in a few hours. Usually, the crystal radio has only four basic parts, a coil, variable capacitor, crystal, and earphones. The coil and capacitor tune in the broadcast station. The fixed or galena crystal rectifies the RF signal, and high-impedance headphones provide audio.

A crystal set has no amplifier, so this sound will not burst your eardrums. High-impedance (1000–2000 ohm) magnetic headphones or crystal earpieces can pick up the weak audio signal. You can build a small IC amplifier for the radio and use an inexpensive set of low-impedance headphones or a speaker. Let's get started and have some fun!

Project 1: The simple crystal radio

What you will need

C1	Sliding tuning capacitor made from PCB material (see text)
L1	25 turns, #24 or #26 enameled wire on 1½-inch form
L2	90 turns, #22 enameled wire
Clips	4 homemade clips from brass or aluminum scrap material

D1   1N34 fixed crystal detector

SW1   Wiping slider made from scrap brass rod or flat
         material

You can easily build a crystal radio from surplus odds and ends. The antenna and tuning coils can be wound on a piece of plastic polyvinyl chloride (PVC) pipe. All clips are made from scraps of brass or aluminum. The sliding tuning capacitor is crafted from double-sided PC copper board. The sliding lever is made from a piece of scrap metal. Even the wooden chassis comes from a piece of scrap ash wood (Fig. 2-1).

Fig. 2-1   *All parts for this project are built from scrap material.*

Although, this crystal radio will not blast out sound or tune stations everywhere on the band, you can listen to a few local AM broadcast stations for only a few bucks. Also, you get to build a radio, and learn how each electronic part works. The sliding capacitor might be rather crude, but it works. You learn how Grandpa built his first radio, and you have just as much fun as he did.

How the circuit works

The circuit is very simple (Fig. 2-2). The antenna signal is picked up by L1 with the outside ground connected to the ground clip. The RF signal is transformed with L2. This large coil winding is

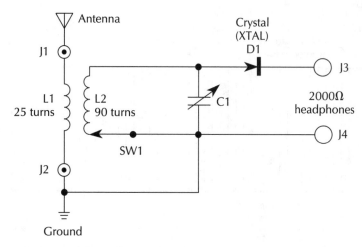

Fig. 2-2 *The small crystal radio, which is a very simple tuning circuit, has only 7 parts.*

tuned by sliding capacitor C1. Switch 1 (SW1) helps to shorten or lengthen the RF coil for station selectivity and separation. The crystal diode (D1) converts the RF signal to audio and connects it to the output posts. The weak audio signal can now be heard with a pair of 2000-ohm headphones.

Winding the coils

For the coil form, pick up a 1½-inch-diameter piece of PVC plastic pipe or fitting at the plumbing department of your local hardware store. Cut a piece 3½ inches long. Drill a ⁵⁄₃₂-inch hole at each end for mounting. Drill all coil wire holes with a PC board (PCB) bit. Start winding L2 from one end towards the other end of the coil form (Fig. 2-3). Leave about 5 inches at the start and finish for wiring connections. Wind 90 turns of #22 enameled wire. The wiper blade area of L2 can be sanded after the coil is mounted.

Space the primary coil (L1) ⅛ inch away from the end of L2. Drill two small holes a half inch apart. Put 25 turns of #24 enameled wire on the remaining area of the coil form. Both coils are close-wound and tight together. Leave 5 or 6 inches of excess at both ends for under-chassis connections (Fig. 2-4). Keep coils in place with cellophane tape or coil dope. Leave excess ends inside coil form until both coils are wound. Mount the coil form with two 1-inch-long, ⁵⁄₃₂-inch-diameter bolts and nuts.

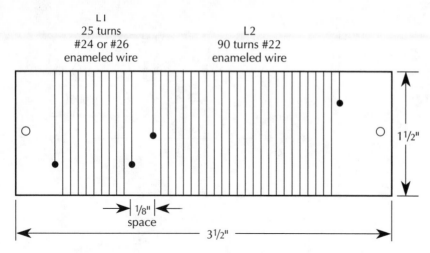

Fig. 2-3 *Wind 90 turns or 2½ inches of #22 enameled wire for L2, and 25 turns of #24 or #26 enameled wire for L1 on a 1½-inch PVC plastic pipe form.*

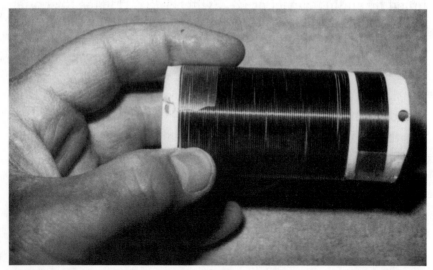

Fig. 2-4 *Drill two ⁵⁄₃₂-inch holes in the bottom side of the coil form to mount on the wood chassis. Sand down the sliding lever area on the coil with sandpaper.*

Making a sliding capacitor

Cut two pieces of double-sided PC board, 3¼ × 3½, with a back-saw or saber saw. Change the saber saw blade to metal. Cut two ½-inch strips of PC board. Then, grind down or file off the ends to ½-inch width (Fig. 2-5). These two thin pieces will support the

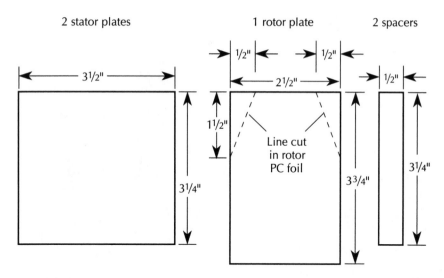

Fig. 2-5 *The sliding tuning capacitor is constructed from double-sided PC board.*

stator capacitor. Mark the bottom with letter B on the outside area for easier assembly.

Next, cut a piece of double-sided PC board 2½ × 3¾ inches long for the rotor. Drill about six ⅛-inch holes to form a slot at the end for a handle. Touch up the slot with a small flat file. File down the PC copper around the edge so that the foil doesn't short against the sides. The rotor piece is tapered either with a saw blade, etched, or ground off with a grinder so the capacitance is low at the end opposite the handle (Fig. 2-6). This sliding capacitor adjusts from 40 pF to 355 pF.

When the rotor piece is inserted ¼ inch, the capacitance should be around 40 to 50 pF. This means the copper plates must be trimmed down. Measure 1½ inches from the rear of the rotor, and over ½ inch. File a cut between the two marks. Make sure the foil is cut on both sides of the board. To prevent breaking the PC board, do not file a groove that is too deep. By leaving the board intact, the rotor is easily tuned without sliding sideways. If too much is taken off, the capacitor won't have at least 355-pF capacitance.

Starting at 40 pF, the capacitance increases to about 150 pF when 1 inch is inserted. With half the rotor inserted, the capacitance jumps to 250 pF, and when fully inserted, the capacitance is around 355 to 375 pF. With this range, C1 can tune in AM stations from 540 to 1450 kHz.

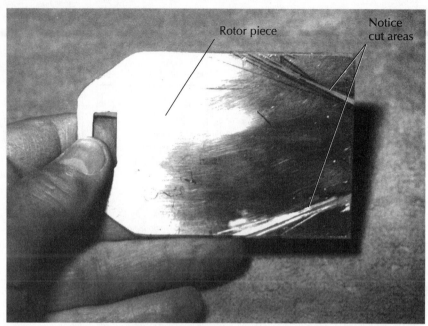

Fig. 2-6   *The rotor, or flat sliding piece, is made from a double-sided board with one end tapered using the edge of a flat file.*

Hold the top and bottom in place with half-inch strips and drill out all holes in each corner. This guarantees the holes match up. Drill one ¾-inch hole from the back to identify the rear and one side of the stator capacitor for easier assembly. Place four ⁶⁄₃₂-inch bolts and nuts in the holes and line up the sides with a grinder or a sander. File off rough edges on the top and bottom plates.

After leveling the sides, remove bolts and nuts and clean off each copper side with steel wool to remove all pencil marks and dirt from the foil areas. Cover the insides of the top and bottom plates with plastic laminating sheets. Make sure each side is clean before applying plastic adhesive. Cut off the excess at the edges with a pocketknife to prevent the rotor from rubbing on the stator plates and shorting out. You can pick up the laminating plastic at most hobby or office supply centers. The same plastic is used to protect newspaper clippings, ID cards, letters, photos, etc. If single-sided copper board is used for top and bottom plates, no plastic insulation is needed.

Reassemble stator parts with bolts and nuts. Make sure the rotor moves back and forth in the slotted opening. Enlarge the holes in the strip pieces using a ⁹⁄₆₄-inch drill bit. Now the inside support pieces can be adjusted so the rotor slides smoothly back and forth without side play. With bolts and nuts in position, lay the capacitor on the wooden chassis and press down or lightly tap with a hammer. Now the holes are marked and can be drilled with a ⁵⁄₃₂-inch bit.

Make sure the rotor slides in and out the opening (Fig. 2-7). Solder a piece of bare hookup wire at the rear on each side to form a bond between the bottom and top plates. This connects the two stator plates together electrically and provides a stop for the rotor piece. Do not connect inside the copper foil together, only the top and bottom outside area. Mount the sliding capacitor to the far right side and flush with the back of the wood chassis. Bolt the capacitor into place with four ⁶⁄₃₂-inch bolts and nuts. A couple of washers can be added to one inside bolt to connect the stator to the tuned circuit.

Fig. 2-7 *The completed sliding capacitor using three pieces of double-sided PC wiring board.*

Making homemade clips

Four separate posts or clips are needed for headphone, antenna, and ground connections. Material can be taken from thin sheets of metal sold at hardware stores. Fahnestock clips can be made from flat brass or aluminum surplus strips. Cut the strips ½ inch wide and 2 inches long. Cut a slot in one end ⅛ inch wide and ¾ inch back. Likewise, cut a ³⁄₁₆-inch-wide and ½-inch-long slot in the other end. These cuts are made in the center of the material (Fig. 2-8).

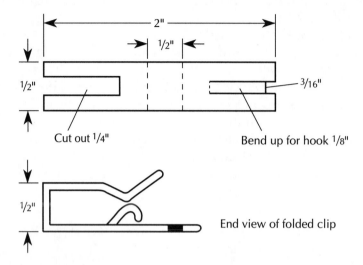

Fig. 2-8 *The homemade phone, antenna, and ground clips are made from scraps of brass or aluminum metal.*

Bend the bottom piece at a width of ⁷⁄₁₆ inch and double the top part back. Form the bottom with an ⅛-inch piece bent upward into a small hook. Make a sharp bend in the top area and cut off any excess material. Bend the top section down so the top hook goes over and around the bottom hook. This area can be adjusted to accept an antenna wire or phone tips. The clips are held in place with a washer and ⁶⁄₃₂-inch bolt and nut. Each clip is connected underneath the chassis.

Building the chassis

Cut a 6-×-8-inch piece of soft wood for the base plate. In this example, the ends of a piece of white ash from a wood project is used. A piece of pine will do. Sand down all edges and slightly round off the corners. Remove all pencil marks. If an electric sander is handy, sand clean the top side of the wood chassis.

Spray on three coats of clear acrylic spray. Let each coat dry before applying the next. Polish the final surface with steel wool. Wipe the chassis clean. Now when handling or drilling holes, the wood chassis does not get dirty. Always place a cloth under the finished chassis while drilling holes.

Drill all holes with a ⅛-inch bit. Place components on the

wooden chassis and mark the required holes. If larger holes are needed, they can easily be drilled from the bottom side. See Fig. 2-9 for details.

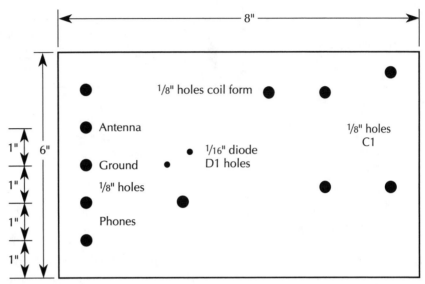

Fig. 2-9 *Drill all required holes on a scrap piece of 1-x-6-x-8-inch wood.*

Mounting parts

The first to be mounted is the sliding capacitor. All components are fastened through the board chassis. If the bolts are not long enough, they can be counter-sunk from the bottom side. Place a washer on each nut to hold connecting wires. A solder lug can be used at the ground terminal for several tie wires. After mounting parts, wire it together (Fig. 2-10).

All wiring is connected under the chassis. The only commercial part used here is the fixed crystal instead of a crystal that uses a cat whisker. Sometimes when moving the rotor plate, the sensitive point of the cat whisker may be moved, so a fixed crystal was used instead. The two crystal ends are fed through small ¹⁄₁₆-inch holes in the chassis. Use a heat sink or long-nose pliers when soldering the crystal wires to dissipate excessive heat. Add stick-on rubber feet to clear small nuts on bottom chassis.

Testing the circuit

Connect the headphones to the output jacks. Connect the antenna and ground wires to their respective clips. Slide the rotor

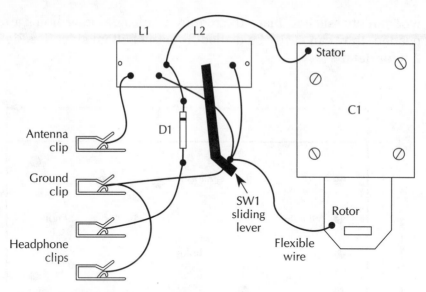

Fig. 2-10 *A pictorial drawing of how the parts are mounted and connected together.*

in and rotate the wiper blade on the coil to place the full coil
winding in the circuit. A local station on the lower band (540
kHz) can be heard. Adjust the wiper blades for the loudest signal.
Touch up the capacitor rotor for final tuning (Fig. 2-11).

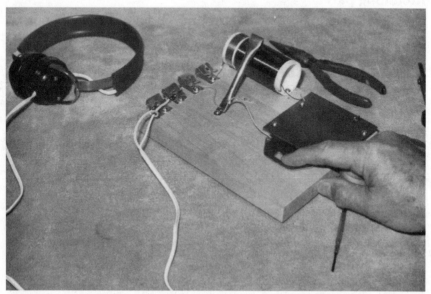

Fig. 2-11 *Tune in a local station with the C1 rotor pushed in, and tune the
slide coil all the way.*

Here we have two local stations, one at 540 kHz and the other at 1400 kHz. To tune in the 1400 station, the rotor is pulled out and the wiper blade is tuned to fewer wires in the circuit. Sometimes clipping the antenna wire to the top of L2 brings in one station louder than the others. A high antenna and good ground is needed for adequate audio reception.

Finish the project up by installing four ½-inch feet cut from a ½-inch wood dowel and glued to the bottom of the wooden base.

Project 2: The spider-web special radio

What you will need

3	Antenna posts (Radio Shack, 274-662; DC Electronics #7004 & 7005)
2	Headphone posts (Radio Shack, 274-662; DC Electronics #7004 & 7005)
C1	365-pF variable capacitor (Antique Electronics Supply, #CV-230; KA7QJY components 365 pF)
L1	21 turns of #22 enameled wire (about 55 feet)
L2	75 turns of #22 enameled wire wound next to L1
1	Pair of 2000-ohm impedance headphones (Antique Electronics Supply #PA-466)
1	Large ¼-inch knob (Radio Shack #274-402)
D1	1N34 fixed crystal diode
SW1	Sliding lever
Misc	Piece of ⅛-inch masonite, 1-inch wood scrap pieces, solid hookup wire, brass dowel, bolts and nuts, solder, screws, etc.

Christopher Columbus proved the world was round despite the fact that expert historians were convinced it was flat. It doesn't matter if the tuning coil is round or flat, they both work. Here you see a flat spider-web coil built right in a radio chassis, (Fig. 2-12).

How the circuit works

To save a few bucks, you can build the tuning coil, tuner slider, and masonite chassis out of scrap material. Winding the coil takes only a few extra minutes, plus it's fun to construct, and it performs like the round ones. Varying the slider on the coil, tuning the capacitor and using different antenna taps provides station selectivity and separation (Fig. 2-13).

Although a crystal stand with cat whiskers might make the ra-

Fig. 2-12 *The crystal radio set is just as exciting to listen to today as it was in Grandpa's day.*

dio appear like the one Grandpa had in the twenties, a fixed germanium diode (1N34) is used in this project. The fixed diode is readily available and is a lot cheaper. With a good outside antenna and high impedance (2000 ohm) headphones, local radio stations can be heard. The low-cost amp at the end of the chapter can drive a small speaker, or low-cost headphones. So, let's get started!

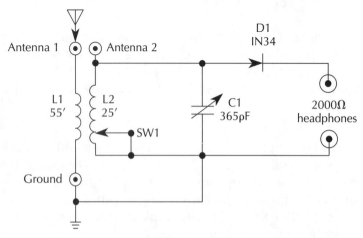

Fig. 2-13 *The spider-web special radio set.*

Winding the coils

Cut off a piece of #22 enameled wire, 55 feet long. Form a loop of transparent tape around the 5-inch end piece and stick it to the bottom side of the masonite slot. All parts can be mounted before applying the top base to the bottom wood supports. Be sure to wind the coil first before mounting any parts.

Start with the long end of the wire and feed it through the next slotted area. Go from slot to slot and wind the coil tight. This means the long end of the coil must be threaded through another slot. Take your time and wind the coil tightly. Flatten the coil wires down, if needed. If the wire is not long enough, make a splice underneath the chassis. Sand down the enameled ends of the wire and trim with solder. Be sure the wire is covered with solder. Lay a piece of wire over each end. Solder the adjoining wires together.

Keep winding the coil to 1½ inches from the outside of the slotted area (Fig. 2-14). You should have approximately 75 turns of wire on the coil. Cut off the lead close to the ground post area. Leave a 5-inch piece to be connected to the ground post. Remember to sand off the enamel on the wire and tin with solder for a good clean electronic connection before connecting. The radio will not work with enameled wire just wrapped around a terminal post.

Fig. 2-14 *The completely wound coil on the masonite form.*

Now wind on 25 feet (ft.) of #22 enameled wire for the primary winding. One end will go to the top antenna post and the other to ground. Notice there are two antenna posts, one for the primary winding, and one at the top of the secondary winding of the coil.

The easiest way to wind on 55 ft. of wire through the slots is to cut the wire off at 30 ft., and push the wire through next to the winding. Pull the loop through by turning the panel over. Make sure all the wire is out. Then push the wire up through the next slot, turn the panel over, and pull the wire through.

Solder the two ends on the back of the panel by laying the wire ends over one another. Scrape off all the enamel covering on the wire and tin with solder. Solder the ends together. You will have only one splice in the middle of the coil.

When pulling wire through the slots, the wire has a tendency to twist and kink up. Just lay the panel down (it will not unwind). Unwind the kinked wire and start again. Wire kinks can be taken out by running wire over a wood pencil with a little pressure at both ends. It will take 2 or 3 hours to wind the coil.

Making the wiper contact

The coil is tuned or switched with a metal sliding blade. The slider is made of a piece of brass or copper. If a flat piece is not handy, pick up a 5/16-inch round brass hollow dowel found at most hobby stores. Place the dowel in a vise and saw it down the middle. Cut a piece 4 inches long and flatten both ends. Round off the end that touches the coil, and drill 1/8-inch hole in the other end (Fig. 2-15).

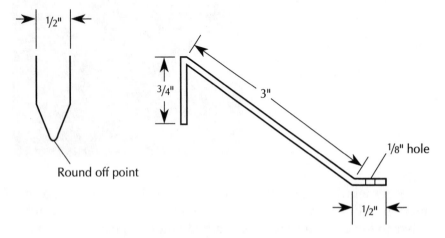

Fig. 2-15 *Construction details of the secondary coil wiper blade.*

File down the rough edges. Either cut or grind off one end to form a smooth, sharp edge for touching the coil. Before mounting the wiper blade, sand down the area of the coil where the wiper blade moves. Now mount the wiper blade. Be sure to apply enough tension on the bolt and nut for a good connection.

Building the chassis

To build the chassis, first cut a piece of masonite to 7×10 inches. Hard masonite is best but any scrap piece will do. Trace the coil outline on the piece of masonite. Center it and lay it out towards the antenna posts. Lay out all holes and slots on the top piece of masonite (Fig. 2-16). Draw a 1-inch round circle in the middle. The edges of the slotted holes can be lined up with a pencil and ruler.

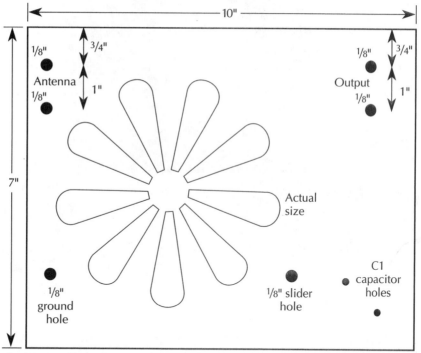

Fig. 2-16 *The chassis layout of the spider-web radio using a piece of masonite. The holes used for mounting parts are shown.*

Drill a ½-inch hole in each outside round slotted area. Drill a ¼-inch hole at the inside circle. The ½-inch hole is used to start the saber saw blade. A hand coping saw will do too, but the power tool is quicker.

Carefully saw out the slotted area between the drilled holes. The slotted areas can be touched up with a flat file and round rat-tail file. Use the flat file on the straight outside areas, and the round file at the ends. Be careful not to break the center section. Make the outside daisy flower ends as round as possible. Sand down the top sides with fine sandpaper and steel wool to eliminate small scratches.

Wipe off both sides of the masonite board to remove any dust or dirt. Spray on three coats of clear acrylic spray. Let each coat dry before applying the next. Apply two coats to the bottom of the masonite. Not only does this provide a protective finish, but it provides electrical insulation. Also, it keeps the wood and masonite surfaces clean (Fig. 2-17).

Fig. 2-17 *The finished masonite chassis and wooden supports with a protective finish of acrylic spray.*

Cut out 2-inch pieces of pine or any soft wood 9⅞ inches long. Then saw two more end pieces of the same thickness 5⅝ inches long. Sand sides and apply two coats of clear acrylic spray. Make sure ends fit and are flush with outside edge of top masonite. Glue and nail the end pieces with one finishing nail. The finished top masonite chassis will screw to the wooden support frame.

Mounting parts

Place the two red antenna posts at the two top left holes, and place a black post at the bottom for ground. Mount the two output posts for the headphones. Bolt the variable capacitor (C1) to the front side of the masonite chassis. Make sure it's lined up straight with the sides of the chassis. The fixed crystal diode is mounted as wired into the circuit. Apply rubber silicone cement or glue to the bottom of the diode to hold it to the chassis. Place a weight over it to hold it in position until it sets.

Wiring the circuit

Use a solder lug on all post connections if available. If not, sand off the ends of the coil wire and tin with solder before forming a loop and wrapping it around the post connections. Connect the primary coil to the top antenna post and the other end to ground (Fig. 2-18). Use a solder lug at the ground post, if possible, since several wires are connected to it. Connect the top secondary winding to the second antenna post and the ground lug.

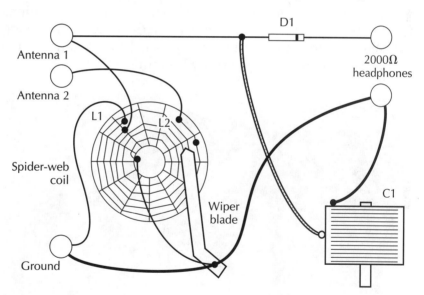

Fig. 2-18 *Pictorial drawing of the wiring for the spider-web special radio.*

Place a ground lug on the bottom side of the wiper blade bolt and solder a wire that goes to the crystal. All wiring is done underneath the masonite. Drill two ⅟₁₆-inch holes for the crystal diode. Push the ends through the holes. Wrap the wire ends together and solder them. Hold the crystal end with a pair of long-nose pliers to act as a heat sink. Otherwise too much heat may ruin the diode. Solder the other crystal end to a wire going to the top output post. Connect a wire to the bottom output post and

solder to the ground lug connection. After wiring, screw the masonite chassis to the wooden supports.

Testing the circuit

Now the spider-web coil radio is ready to test. Connect the outside antenna wire to the top (primary) post. Connect a good
ground wire to the bottom (black) ground post. Rotate the wiper
blade to the end of the secondary coil. Leave the tuning capacitor fully meshed.

Insert headphone jacks (2000 ohms) into the post. If a set of
2000-ohm impedance headphones are not available, connect the
small power amplifier, then use a pair of 8–50-ohm headphones.

Start tuning C1 until a station is heard. When the capacitor
plates are fully meshed, the broadcast frequency is around 520
kHz (Fig. 2-19). When the capacitor plates are open, the broadcast stations can be heard. To prevent strong broadcast stations
from interfering with weaker stations, use the primary or the top
of the coil antenna post for best reception. Tune in and out stations with the wiper blades. Happy Listening!

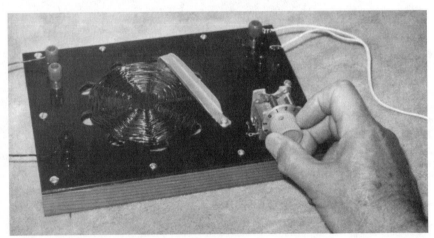

Fig. 2-19 *Stations on the lower end of the dial (540 MHz) can be tuned in
with C1 plates meshed and the wiper blade tuned out to the edge
of the coil.*

Project 3: The switching capacitance radio

What you will need

D1	1N34 germanium fixed-crystal diode
L1	25 turns, #24 or #26 enameled wire on ferrite

	rod, 5 inches long, 0.333 inch diameter (Antique Electronics Supply PC-185)
L2	105 turns, #24 or #26 enameled wire
C1	365-pF variable capacitor (Antique Electronics Supply CF-230 KA7QJy or Components 365 pF.
C2	150-pF capacitor (DC Electronics, 110COG151, 50V or Antique Supply, 150 pF)
C3	270-pF capacitor, (DC Electronics, 110COG271, 50V or Antique Supply, 250 pF
C4	470-pF capacitor (DC Electronics, 110COG4715, 50V or Antique Supply, 500 pF)
C5	1000-pF capacitor (DC Electronics, 110COG102K, 50V or Antique Supply, 1000 pF)
J1, J2, J3, J4	Terminal posts. (All Electronics #5-BP-B black, #5-BP-R red, or Radio Shack, 274-662)
SW1	Single-pole, 4-position rotary switch (Radio Shack, 275-1385 or DC Electronics, #10YX018)
SW2	Single-pole, 5-position rotary switch (Radio Shack, 275-1385 or DC Electronics, #10YX018)
Misc.	Cabinet and chassis board and panel, hookup wire, solder, ⅝₂-inch bolts and nuts, knobs, etc.

Although this crystal radio circuit is somewhat similar to the previous sets we built, all switching is accomplished with two separate switches. The primary winding (L1) of the fixed capacitors may help to separate annoying stations. L2 is tapped, and can be switched in and out of the circuit to tune various areas of the broadcast band. C2 is the main tuning capacitor (Fig. 2-20).

How the circuit works

The broadcast signal is picked up with the antenna and inducted by L2. The RF signal is selected with switch SW2 and capacitor C1 (Fig. 2-21). C1 tunes in the local AM broadcast program. L1 and L2 are wound on a ferrite iron core. Switch SW1 switches in different fixed capacitances to eliminate unwanted stations.

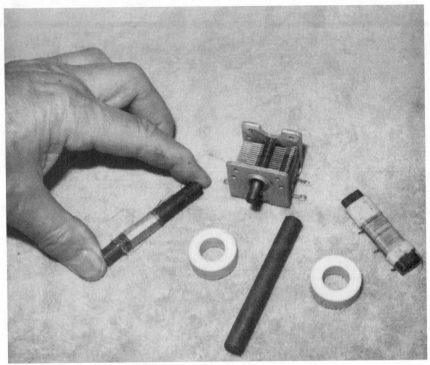

Fig. 2-20 *The ferrite iron core coil and a variable tuning capacitor bring in local radio stations.*

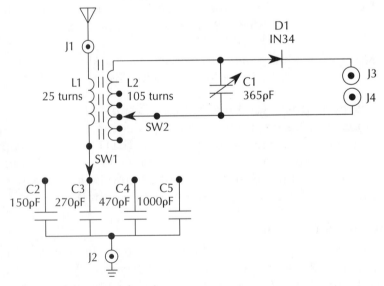

Fig. 2-21 *A switched-crystal radio showing switches SW1 and SW2.*

The cost of the receiver is kept to a minimum because it uses only one variable capacitor.

D1 can be either a fixed crystal diode or a crystal stand with cat whiskers to change the selected RF signal to audio. The audio signal is heard with either crystal or 2000-ohm high-impedance headphones. The switching capacitance set audio output signal can be connected to the audio amplifier at the end of this chapter.

Winding the coils

Select a 5-inch-long 0.333-inch-diameter ferrite form for about $2–$3. Wind 105 turns of #24 or 26 enameled wire onto the form for L2 (Fig. 2-22). In the middle, place one layer of transparent tape and wind on 25 turns of the same size wire for L1. Leave about 5 inches at each end. Use tape over the coil wire to hold it in place while coil dope or model plastic cement is applied. Ferrite or iron core forms produce a high "Q" and may be more selective than air-plastic pipe forms.

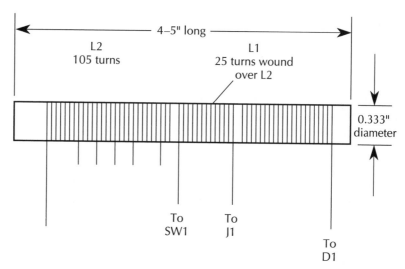

Fig. 2-22 *Wind the coil on a ferrite rod 5 inches long. Ferrite rods can be found at surplus stores or ordered from electronic mailing parts companies.*

If a 5-inch length is not available, you can get by with a form 3 inches long. Use smaller wire for the shorter form length. Many of these rods can be found in surplus markets (Fig. 2-23). The coil form may be mounted to the wooden chassis with rubber silicone cement.

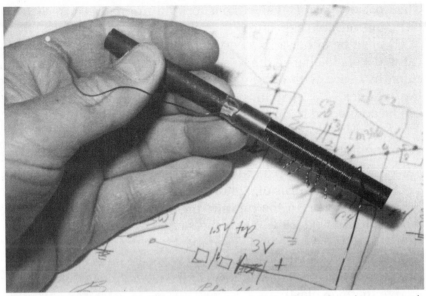

Fig. 2-23 *Closeup view of the completely wound coil, ready to be mounted.*

When winding the ferrite broadcast coil, wind 10 turns, then twist the wire in a short loop about six times. Then wind another 10 turns and twist another tap. Leave the twisted end sticking out about ½ inch. It is easier to wind the rest of the coil if the tap windings are bent over and out of the way. Keep the turns close together, especially at the twisted wire tap. Try to keep the taps in the same area on the coil. Wind the coil tightly.

L1 can be wound over the clear area of the coil, away from the various taps. To wind L1, place a layer of tape over about one inch of coil area. You use transparent tape to keep the ends from unraveling. Then apply coil dope, model cement, or rubber silicone cement. Let it set for an hour or so.

Make sure all taps have a good connection. Scrape enamel off of the wire taps with a pocketknife. Apply rosin core paste, then solder the wire taps. You can tell when the taps are soldered thoroughly because the wire shines and becomes one wire. Do a continuity check with the ohmmeter. You should have a measurement under 0.7-ohm resistance.

Building the chassis

For this switched-capacitance set an L-type chassis is made up of a plastic or masonite front with a 1-inch wooden base. Cut a piece of soft pine 4½ × 7 inches for the main chassis. Sand down all edges. Cut a front piece 5 × 8 inches. Switches SW1, SW2, and capacitor C1 can be mounted on the front panel (Fig. 2-24). If C1 mounts at the bottom, only a ¼-inch shaft hole is needed for the tuning capacitor. Cut off the switch shafts to stick out about ⁵⁄₁₆ inch from the front panel.

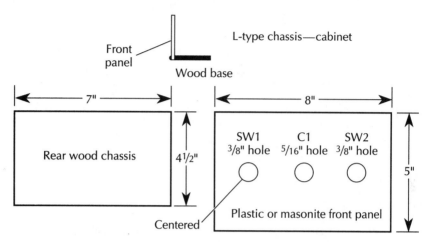

Fig. 2-24 *Front panel and rear chassis layout of holes with* L-*type cabinet.*

Line up SW1, SW2, and C1 in the center of the front panel with pointer or indicator type knobs. Dial markings can be placed on C1 showing exact locations of local stations. Likewise, the two switches can be numbered. Front panel lettering should be sprayed with acrylic spray. Also spray two coats on the wooden base. Secure the front panel to the base chassis with three wood screws.

Mounting parts

Mount the coil on the back of SW1 and SW2 to the base. Connect all taps to SW2. Start with number 1 switch position at the bottom end of the coil form (Fig. 2-25). Solder the tap wire of L2 to D1. Use a pair of long-nose pliers so as not to damage D1 with excessive heat. Connect the common switching terminal of SW2 to the rotor terminal of C1. The stator capacitor terminal is connected to the high side of the coil and the crystal diode. Solder a wire from D1 to the J3 audio output post. Connect J4 to a common ground wire. All connections are made above the chassis.

The top side of the primary winding of L1 goes to the antenna post (J1). Wire the bottom coil wire to the common switch

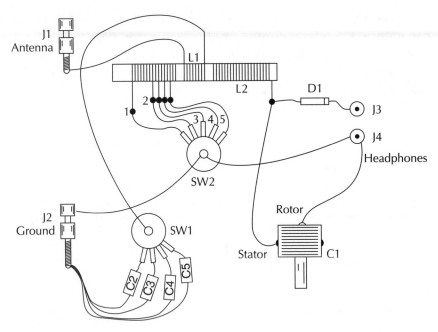

Fig. 2-25 *How the various parts are mounted and wired.*

terminal of SW1. Solder one end of C2, C3, C4 and C5 to the ground terminal. Start with C2 and connect to terminal 1 of SW1. Likewise, solder each capacitor. Double check each wire and part for correct connections. Solder all connections on components and connecting wires.

Testing the circuit

Connect the outside antenna and ground to the respective posts on the circuit, and connect headphones at the output posts. Turn the tuning capacitor to the desired frequency band area. For example, if one local station is at 1400 kHz, turn C1 wide open, SW2 at position 5 and SW1 at position 4.

If a crystal stand with cat whiskers is used, try to locate a sensitive spot on the galena crystal area. Several tries may be needed to find the hottest point. Of course, if a fixed diode is used, no additional adjustment is needed. Rotate both SW1 and SW2 to help separate interfering stations.

When a station is tuned to the low broadcast band (540 kHz), you will find that tuning capacitor C1 is fully meshed, and SW2 is at position 1. Rotate SW1 to help eliminate other stations or to improve the signal. If you have built both crystal set number 1 and this circuit, notice the difference between the two sets in sensitivity and selectivity of the local broadcast stations. Glue on ½-inch wood screw hole plugs on the wooden chassis for feet. You're finished! This set was fun to build!

Project 4: The permeability-tuned radio

What you will need

L1	25 turns, #24 or #26 enameled wire on ferrite rod 0.330 inch diameter × 5 inches long (Antique Electronics Supply, PD-185 or Amidon, R61-050-400)
L2	97 turns, #24 or 26 enameled wire
C1 & C2	365-pF variable capacitors (Antique Electronics Supply CV-230 or KA7QJY Components, 365 pF
D1	1N34 fixed crystal diode
2	2 push-button terminal strips (Radio Shack, #274-315 or Hosfelt Electronics, 2-878)
Misc.	Wood base, masonite or plastic front, bolts & nuts, solder, hookup wire, etc.

The permeability-tuned radio coil is wound on a 5-inch-long ferrite rod. These rods can be ordered through mail-order firms or taken from a scrapped tube radio. The circuit is called a permeability-tuned set because it is tuned by moving the iron core within the magnetic field of the coil. Some of the early small radios have a flat ferrite rod antenna coil called a "loop stick." If one of these coils is used, it must be tuned with a 150-pF tuning capacitor. By winding your own coil on a ferrite rod, the coil is tuned with a 365-pF variable capacitor.

After the coil is wound, it can be mounted on the back of the front panel with rubber silicone cement (Fig. 2-26). Push-button (2 terminal) speaker strips are used as antenna and ground with the same type strip for the output posts. These terminal strips can be mounted on the front panel also.

How the circuit works

The tuned crystal radio circuit is similar to the switching capacitance set except that C1 is connected in the leg of L1 for tuning stations. The high "Q" coil (L2) is tapped at the 67th turn from ground and the tap connects to the crystal rectifier (D1) (Fig. 2-27). The secondary coil (L2) is tuned by C2. C2 selects the broad-

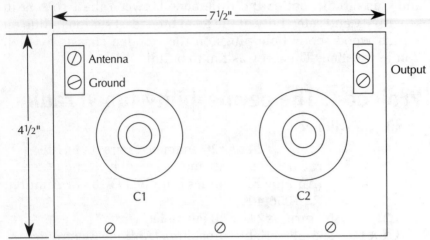

Fig. 2-26 *The permeability-tuned crystal radio can be built on an L-type chassis with a wooden base and masonite or plastic front.*

cast stations, while C1 adds signal, and tunes unwanted stations to ground.

The output terminal strip connects the rectified signal to the red terminal and ground is at the black terminal. This crystal radio can be connected to the audio amplifier at the end of this chapter for small speaker or headphone operation. Otherwise, use a 2000-ohm impedance headphone or a crystal earphone for audio reception.

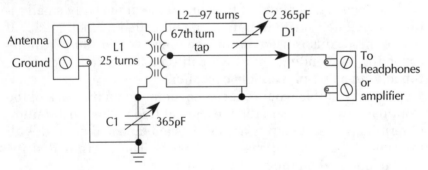

Fig. 2-27 *Schematic of the permeability-tuned radio set.*

Winding the coils

Start at the ground end and hold the coil winding in place with transparent tape. Keep the wire taut to make it close wound on the ferrite rod. At the 67th turn, twist the wire about 5 times and then continue to wind the remaining wire on the form for a total of 97 turns for L2. Wind both coils with #24 or 26 enameled wire (Fig. 2-28).

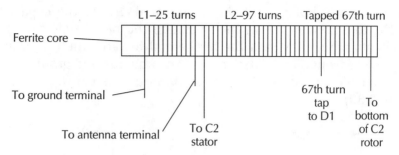

Fig. 2-28 *L1 & L2 coil winding information. Wire both coils with #24 or 26 enameled wire.*

Place a layer of tape over the center of L2 and wind 25 turns for L1. Leave about 5 inches of coil wire to be connected to other components. Place tape at the beginning and at the end of winding the coil to prevent unraveling. Regular coil dope or clear fingernail polish will hold the coil wire in place also (Fig. 2-29).

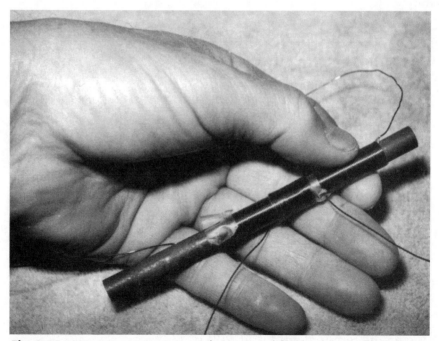

Fig. 2-29 *Use transparent tape at the start and finish of the coil winding to keep it from unraveling.*

Mounting parts

Both tuning capacitors (C1 & C2) are mounted on the front panel. If the variable capacitors only have base mounting holes, make cabinet holes to fit the front panel. Allow the capacitor shafts to extend ⁵⁄₁₆ of an inch through the panel hole for each knob attachment. Mount the ferrite coil towards the center and top of the front panel. Also, mount the antenna and ground connection on the left, and the headphone jack strip on the right (Fig. 2-30).

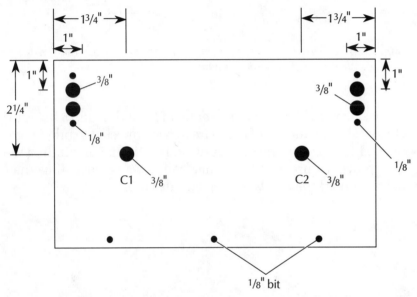

Fig. 2-30   *Layout of parts on the front panel. Most of the drilled holes require a ⅜-inch bit.*

Drill ⅜-inch holes for the two variable capacitors. Drill two ⅜-inch holes for each set of terminal strips. These strips can be placed on the front panel and the required holes can be marked off. The soldered lugs must have enough room to sit flat on the front panel. D1 is mounted as it is wired into the circuit.

Wiring the circuit

Run the top side of antenna (L1) wire to the red lug on the antenna strip. The bottom side of L1 can be soldered to the stator lug of C1. Connect a wire from the rotor of C1 to the black round lug on the terminal strip (Fig. 2-31).

Connect the top side of L2 to the stator terminal of C2, and

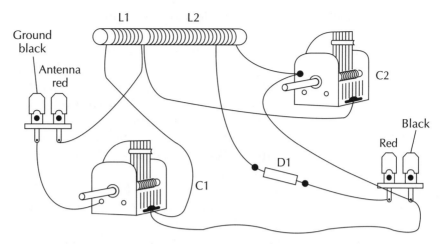

Fig. 2-31 *How to connect the permeability-tuned radio.*

the bottom wire to the rotor terminal. Solder a hookup wire to the top of the coil, and connect to the RF rectifier (D1). The other end of D1 goes to the red lug on the output strip. Connect a ground wire from the black lug of the terminal strip to the stator lug on C1. Double check all wiring. Nothing is more disappointing than when your radio project doesn't work.

Testing the circuit

Rotate C2 to your favorite local station, then tune in C1 for clarity and sensitivity. Tune in a station at the low end of the dial, with C2 fully meshed. Rotate C2 to locate the station. Adjust C1 to eliminate any other stations and improve local radio reception.

If a crystal stand and galena crystal are used in place of a fixed diode (D1), try to locate the hot spot on the crystal surface. It might take several attempts. Some areas are hotter than others on the surface. Add a small audio amplifier for greater volume. The amplifier can be mounted on the back of the wooden chassis.

Project 5: The deluxe TRF radio

What you will need

D1 & D2	1N34 fixed crystal diodes
C2 & C3	Dual-gauged 365-pF variable capacitors (Antique Electronics Supply, CV-240 or use one taken from an old antique radio)
C1	Single-section 365-pF variable capacitor

	(Antique Electronics Supply, CV-230 or KA7QSY Components 365 pF)
C1A & C2A	40- to 50-pF trimmer capacitors (Antique Electronics Supply CF-421 or Radio Shack 276-168. These capacitors may not be needed if already mounted on the dual-variable capacitors)
L1	40 turns, #24 or #26 enameled wire
L2 & L3	87 turns, #24 or #26 enameled magnet wire wound on ferrite rod
2	2 terminal strips (Radio Shack, 274-315)
1	Ferrite antenna rod 0.333-inch diameter and 5 inches long
Misc.	Masonite panel, wood base, bolts and nuts, hookup wire, small wood screws, solder, etc.

The tuned-RF frequency (TRF) radio was built back in the early 1930's. Some of these radios had two or three tuned RF stages. This project uses two tuned-RF stages with two separate secondary RF coils, and one dual capacitor. Full-wave rectification is provided with D1 and D2. The two RF circuits are coupled with L1 and C1, providing variable selectivity in a high "Q" circuit (Fig. 2-32).

Fig. 2-32   *The TRF crystal radio is easy to operate because it uses two different variable capacitors.*

How the circuit works

The broadcast signal is picked up by the outside antenna and appears at J1 and RF coil L1 (Fig. 2-33). C1 provides a ground wave-

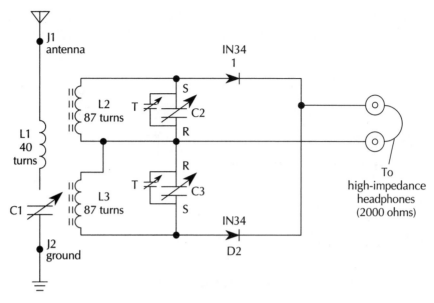

Fig. 2-33 *This circuit requires several more components to accomplish full-wave rectification of the RF signal.*

trap to eliminate unwanted stations. This capacitor also provides maximum gain to coils L2 and L3. Both L2 and L3 are wound with the same number of turns (87) on the outside of L1. These two secondary windings are tuned with a dual 365-pF variable capacitor.

The RF signal is coupled from L1 to L2, and L3 provides a full-wave tuned circuit. Both C2 and C3 provide maximum signal to diodes D1 and D2. The two outside coil leads of L2 and L3 are connected to the fixed crystal diodes. The high-impedance magnetic headphones pick up the full-wave audio signal at J3 and J4.

Winding the coils

All three coils are wound on a single ferrite core. The ferrite or powdered iron core provides high "Q" tuned circuit. This is more selective than a low "Q" circuit wound on a PVC plastic pipe or cardboard form. Ferrite cores have a higher "Q" factor in the high-frequency range when smaller forms are used. Likewise, in the low-frequency range, higher "Q" can be achieved when using the larger core.

Select a ferrite rod, at least 5 inches long, so that all three coils can be wound on it. These coils are wound with #24 or #26 enameled magnet wire (Fig. 2-34). All coils are close wound on the ferrite rod. The primary winding is found between L2 and L3 on the ferrite rod.

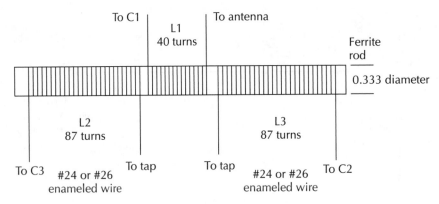

Fig. 2-34 *Coil information for the deluxe TRF radio.*

Start at one end and wind 87 turns of #24 or #26 enameled wire for L2. Use transparent tape at the starting end to hold the wire in place. You can start by looping tape over the wire, placing it on the rod, and winding wire over the excess tape. When finishing the coil end of L2, again place tape over the winding. Just a ¼-inch strip is all that's needed. Coil dope, clear fingernail polish, rubber silicone cement, or plastic model cement can also be used after the coils are wound. (Fig. 2-35).

Now, wind coil L1 about ⅛ inch from the finished winding of L2. Wind on 40 turns of the same size wire. Tape both ends so the coil doesn't unravel.

For L3, wind on another 87 turns. All coils are wound with the same wire and in the same direction. Space L3 about ⅛ inch from the end of L1. Leave about 6 inches of existing wire on all coil ends for easy connections. The coil wires can be tinned and cut to length after the coil form is mounted. After all coils are wound, secure each coil end with cement. Let the coil cement set for one hour before mounting in the chassis (Fig. 2-36).

Building the chassis

Cut a piece of soft pine or ash wood 5 × 8 inches for the rear chassis. Drill all required holes with a ⁵⁄₃₂-inch bit. Determine where dual-variable capacitors C2 and C3 will be mounted. Mount C1 on the left side of the front panel. The front panel can be either a

Fig. 2-35   *Closeup view of how the coils are wound.*

Fig. 2-36   *Coil mounted on the front panel with rubber silicone cement.*

piece of hard masonite or plastic. If you want the front panel to have an antique appearance, use a piece of phenolic black panel. These panels were used in the early days of battery radio.

Saw 5 × 9½ inches of masonite or plastic material for the front panel. Drill all required holes in the front and rear chassis (Fig. 2-37 and Fig. 2-38). Holes for the antenna, ground and output post can be made on the rear wooden base. Finish the wood chassis and front masonite panel with three coats of acrylic spray. Let dry between each coat. Transfers for numbers and dial markings can be added after the first coat. After all wiring is completed, glue on ½-inch wood screw hole plugs for feet on the rear chassis.

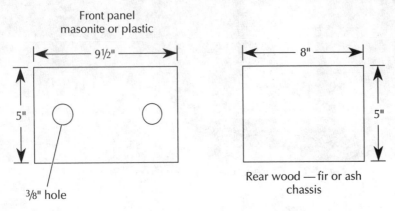

Fig. 2-37   *Required dimensions for the front panel.*

Mounting parts

Mount the coil form towards the top of the chassis, above and centered over both capacitors. Secure the ferrite rod with silicone rubber cement at each end. Use enough cement so the coil does not come loose.

Place the antenna post or terminal strip on the left side with two small wood screws. Fasten the twin output jacks in the same manner. Mount the two variable capacitors on the front panel. Make sure the shaft hole is big enough to fit the raised area surrounding the shaft. Be careful that the front screws are not so long that they interfere with the stator or the rotor plates.

Testing the circuit

After all components have been wired up, go over the wiring once again. Now the fun begins! Hook up the antenna and ground wires. Clip the headphones onto the output posts. Rotate the dual capacitor (C1 and C2) until a station is heard at the center of the band. If C1 and C2 use trimmer capacitors, adjust for maximum volume. If C1 and C2 have no trimmer capacitors, put C1 and C2 in parallel with trimmer capacitors to get 6- to 50-pF capacitance (Fig. 2-39).

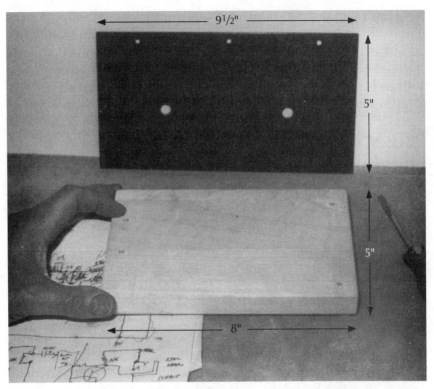

Fig. 2-38 *Required dimensions for the wooden base and front panel.*

Fig. 2-39 *Place the trimmer capacitors across each variable capacitor for tuning the maximum RF signal for a local station.*

Adjust C1 on the antenna RF coil for maximum volume on a tuned station in the center of the broadcast band. Readjust the trimmer capacitors for maximum volume. If a local station is not heard at the center of the band, pick out the weakest station and adjust the coils and the trimmer capacitors for maximum selectivity. This TRF receiver works well with the small IC amplifier and headphones.

Project 6:
Headphone and speaker amplifier

What you will need

C1 & C3	10-µF, 25-V electrolytic capacitor
C2	0.1-µF, 100-V ceramic capacitor
C4 & C6	220-µF, 25-V electrolytic capacitor
C5	0.047-µF, 100-V ceramic capacitor
R1	10-kilohm audio tapered control with single-pole, single-throw switch, with a PC boardmount
R2	10-ohm, ½-watt resistor
J1	Mono headphone jack
IC1	LM386 audio IC
Misc.	8-pin IC DIP socket, a scrap piece of double-sided PC board, bolts and nuts, solder, etc.
SW1	Single-pole, single-throw switch
B1	9V battery

The little IC amplifier (amp) in Fig. 2-40 can be built on a PC strip or on a multi-purpose board. It can be connected to any one of the previous crystal sets, or to the tube radios for added volume. The volume control, all parts, and 9-V battery are fastened on the PC strip.

The amp output impedance connects directly to the 8-ohm permanent magnet (PM) speaker, or to a jack for an 8- to 32-ohm pair of headphones. In fact, you can operate a cheap pair of headphones (under $5), and build the entire amp for less than the cost of a pair of 2000-ohm headphones. So add this small amp to your favorite crystal set and have plenty of volume and clear reception with an inexpensive pair of headphones or a speaker.

How the circuit works

The simple operational (OP) amplifier circuit is built around a small 8-pin IC. LM386 operates from a 9-volt battery. The audio signal input is fed to the top of R1 (10K), which is an audio-

Fig. 2-40 *The completed headphone or speaker amp, ready to be connected to a crystal set or a one-tube radio.*

tapered volume control. The center control of R1 is coupled through C1 (10 µF) to pin 3 of IC1 with the audio input signal (Fig. 2-41).

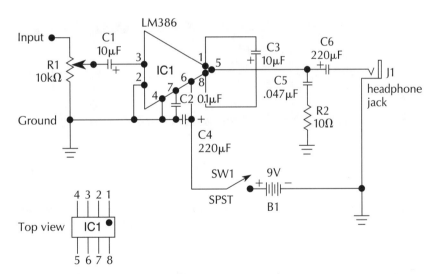

Fig. 2-41 *The small IC amp.*

The audio signal is amplified by IC1 and fed out through terminal 5. Capacitor C6 couples the amplified audio to the output headphone or speaker jack (J1). C2 and C4 are bypass capacitors. C4 should be mounted close to pin 6 of IC1 to prevent interference.

SW1 applies the 9-volt battery voltage to the voltage supply (pin 6). Connect about 4 inches of flexible hookup wire to the PC board, so J1 can be mounted on the front panel, if needed. All the parts, except for J1, mount directly on the PC strip.

Laying out the board

The PC layout is the actual size of the PC board, which is 4½ × 1½ inches. R1 is mounted towards the front, with the 9-volt battery at the rear of the board. Trace or lay out the exact PC wiring as shown in Fig. 2-42. Place a wide ground strip on the top side of the double PC board to help strengthen the board. Lay out holes on the opposite side of the foil from R1 to strengthen the PC terminals because they are on a double-sided board. Larger holes are used on R1 terminals.

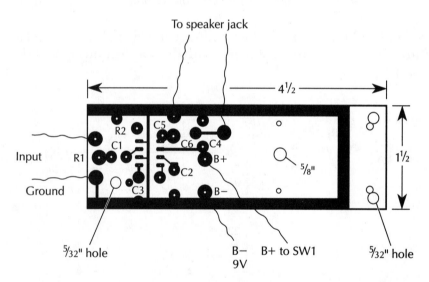

Fig. 2-42 *The simple PC board layout of the small amp. The layout can be copied on to a scrap piece of double-sided PC board.*

After the small board is etched (it should only take three-quarters of an hour at most), drill small PC holes in all circles. Lay a wooden block under the PC board while drilling. Make sure the bit goes through the PC board to prevent a bump on the opposite side. Drill the battery holder and PC mount holes with a ⁵⁄₃₂-inch bit.

Soldering the circuit

Drop the various components in the correct holes and solder them. Leave the volume control as the last part to be mounted so you won't damage the PC board or crack the wiring. Make sure it is level when soldering terminals.

Double check each contact for a good solder joint, and to be sure no solder has dripped over the circuits. Take continuity measurements with an ohmmeter. Check the IC terminals and wiring with a magnifying glass. Sometimes small PC wiring breaks where it connects to the part (Fig. 2-43). Mount the volume control by twisting the lugs over the front end of the board, then solder it.

Fig. 2-43 *With its small size, the completed project can mount most anywhere. Check all wiring and joints before turning on the amp.*

Testing the circuit

Attach the 9-volt battery clips. Snap the battery into its holder. Clip the IC into the socket. Connect the amp to one of the crystal sets. Insert your headphones. Sit back and enjoy!

If there is no response from the amp, suspect poor connections or that the IC is in backwards. Check the white dot for pin 1. A white matching dot can be placed on both sides of the board (at pin 1) with typing correction fluid. Measure the voltage at the various pins. Compare these measurements with those on the schematic. Double check all wiring. You should hear a click in the headphones when a screwdriver blade touches the center terminal of R1.

Take a current measurement of IC1. Remove one clip of the 9-volt battery, and turn the other clip halfway around. Insert the milliamp meter between the two exposed battery and socket terminals. Another method to measure current is to measure current across the switch terminals with the switch OFF. When connected, IC1 should have a current measurement of 5.8 milliamperes (mA) (Fig. 2-44). If it draws over 10 mA, suspect a defective IC or a leaky C4. To be sure, check the wiring and solder joints once again.

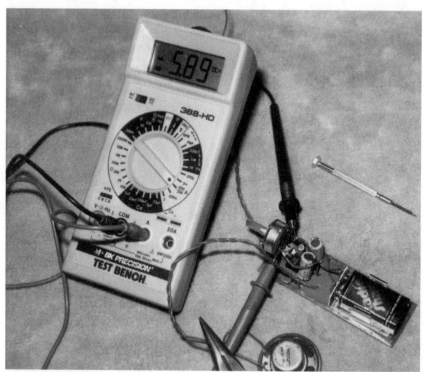

Fig. 2-44 *Excessive current drain may indicate a defective IC or an IC mounted backwards. The correct current of idle amplifiers is only in the milliampere range.*

❖3
AM radio projects

BESIDES THE CRYSTAL SET, EARLY AM RADIOS WERE ALSO BUILT using one or two tubes. Many consisted of only RF, detector, and amplifier stages. Large tube receivers used ac power. Before World War II, the five-tube radio became famous. After World War II, the portable transistor radio started a new era in radio listening.

The first transistor radio constructed consisted of a crystal detector and transistor amplifier. Next came the regeneration and superhet circuits. Today, integrated circuits (ICs), varactor diode tuning, and PC boards (PCBs) have generated much excitement.

Surface-mounted components have made the commercial receiver smaller, so it can fit in any circuit. You can still have a lot of fun building transistor-, IC-, and varactor-tuning AM radios. Let's give one a try!

Project 1: The linear IC AM radio

What you will need

IC1	ZN414, Ferranti IC (DC Electronics, ZN414 or Circuit Specialists, ZN414)
Q1	2N3904 low-power transistor
Ferrite rod	⅜ × 4 inches, (Antique Electronics Supply, PC- 185)
VD1	275-pF variable capacitance diode (Hosfelt Electronics, MV1662 or Oak Hills Research, MV1662)
C1, C1A, C4 & C5	0.1-µF, 50-V ceramic capacitor
C2 & C3	0.01-µF, 50-V ceramic capacitor
C6	10-µF, 50-V electrolytic capacitor
L1	70 turns, #26 enameled wire
R1	47-kilohm, ½-watt-resistor

R2	10-kilohm linear tapered control
R3	100-kilohm, ½-watt resistor
R4, R5, R6	1-kilohm, ½-watt resistor
R7	15-kilohm, ½-watt resistor
R8	10-kilohm, ½-watt resistor
SW1	Single-pole, single-throw
Misc.	3-×-4½-inch PCB, stereo headphone jack, solder, knob, screws, wood cabinets, etc.
B1	9-V battery

AM radios come in many sizes and shapes. They are built in clocks, in fuzzy rabbits, they come in table models, and can be a combination of AM and FM. This simple radio is built around a Ferranti linear integrated IC (ZN414). The ZN414 is a 10-transistor, tuned-radio frequency (TRF) circuit packaged in a 3-pin TO-18 transistor case. The whole radio unit is built inside a scrap piece of 2 × 4 pine or fir wood (Fig. 3-1).

Fig. 3-1 *Here is a slick-looking AM radio built on a regular 2-×-4-inch piece of wood.*

IC1 consists of a very high-impedance stage, several RF stages, and an automatic gain control (AGC) transistor and detector, all mounted in a small plastic transistor case. Terminal 2 is the input, terminal 3 is ground, and terminal 1 is the audio output terminal (Fig. 3-2). This small IC operates from 1.2 to 1.6 volts dc.

How the circuit works

The TRF front end has a 70-turn enameled wire coil wound on a ferrite rod with varactor tuning (Fig. 3-3). Varactor diode 1 (VD1),

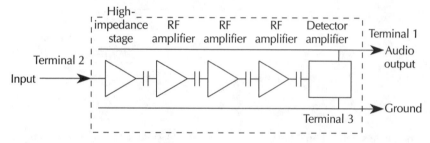

Fig. 3-2   *This small radio is built around a linear integrated circuit (IC1).*

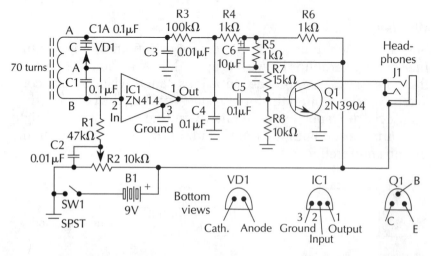

Fig. 3-3   *The complete schematic diagram of the linear IC radio with IC1 as the RF circuit, detector circuit, and amplifier, with a single transistor output stage.*

instead of a variable air capacitor, provides AM tuning. Side B of the coil is fed directly into the input of IC1 (pin 2). Side A connects to the low-voltage side of the circuit and uses several voltage dividers. Capacitors C1 and C1A isolate the varactor diode from the voltage of the tuning circuit. Resistors R3, R4, R5, R6 and capacitor C6 provide low voltage to IC1 from a 9-volt battery source.

Although the IC1 audio output (pin 1) can operate a pair of 2000-ohm headphones, another audio stage was added. Capacitor C5 couples the audio signal to the base terminal of Q1 (2N3904). A low-cost crystal headphone can be used if you add a resistor (Fig. 3-4). If the small IC audio amp is attached to the linear IC radio, change the headphone jack to a 10-kΩ resistor and add a 10-μF electrolytic capacitor coupled to the amp input. A pair of low-impedance phones may be used at headphone jack (J1).

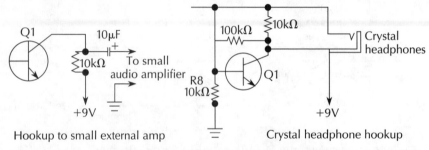

Hookup to small external amp   Crystal headphone hookup

Fig. 3-4 *You can use a low-impedance headphone, a 2000-ohm headphone, or a crystal headphone by simply modifying the output circuit.*

Winding the coils

Select a ⅜-inch-diameter ferrite core 4 or 5 inches long. Wrap a piece of tape around the wire (Fig. 3-5). Leave about 4 inches of the core bare. Position the wire taps lengthwise on the core. Wrap the wire around the form to start winding the coil. Wind L1 right over the tape next to the first winding. Keep the wire tight and turn the rod with the right hand. Feed the wire between the thumb and forefinger.

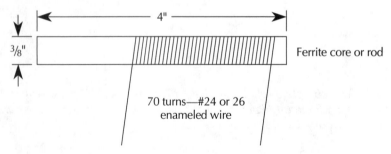

Fig. 3-5 *Wind 70 turns of #26 enameled wire over a 4-inch ferrite rod. Hold each end with tape until the coil dope or cement dries.*

Wind on about 70 turns of #24 or 26 enameled wire. The coil should take up about 3 to 3½ inches on the form. When reaching the end, place a layer of tape over the wire to keep it taut, and to prevent it from unraveling. Drop on coil dope or clear fingernail polish at both ends. Silicone rubber cement will also hold the wire in position. After all wiring is complete, mount the coil at the top of the PCB.

Laying out the PC board

The front panel of the linear IC radio consists of a PC board cut to 3 × 6⅜ inches. All parts are mounted on the back of the PC board. The largest component on the board is R2, which tunes the broadcast band.

Lay out the PC wiring as shown in Fig. 3-6. The outside area of the board is at ground potential. Do not drill any holes in the board after the PC board (PCB) is etched. Remember, all parts are mounted or tacked on the wiring from the PC wiring side. The front has a copper outside line made with ½-inch-wide tape. Place tape on before etching the board. The only holes drilled in the PCB are those that hold the board to the finished wooden 2-×-4-inch frame. Drill ⅜-inch holes for R2 and the headphone jack.

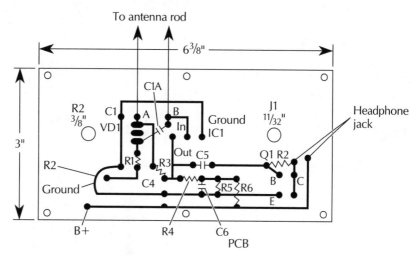

Fig. 3-6 *Lay out the PC wiring as shown. All parts, except the battery, are placed on the rear of the PC board.*

Mounting parts

All components are mounted to the PC wiring by bending over each terminal in an L fashion. Mount each part as close to the board as possible. Solder in all small capacitors and resistors. Then solder in IC1, Q1 and VD1. Use the long-nose pliers as a heat sink so as not to damage the solid-state devices. Cut the part leads as short as possible and bend an L at each end for easy soldering.

Mount the headphone jack and connect the hookup wire from the jack to the L terminals. Likewise, mount the R2 (10 kΩ) tuning control and connect wires from each lug to the respective PC wiring. L1 is mounted above and away from the chassis. Fasten the ferrite rod to the cabinet with rubber silicone cement at each end. Solder the coil wires to the A and B terminals on the PC board. Keep all ground leads as short as possible.

Building the chassis

Select a fairly new scrap of fir wood, about 2 × 4 inches for the cabinet. Lay out the dimensions of the PCB on one side. Leave ¼-inch lip so the six screws can hold the PCB to the front piece of wood. Drill one ½-inch bit hole in each corner. Cut out the outline with a coping or saber saw. This piece of wood is thick, so don't rush it (Fig. 3-7).

Fig. 3-7 *This small cabinet was cut out of a scrap piece of fir or pine wood about 2 × 4 inches long. Drill and cut out an opening so the PC board fits over the enclosed parts.*

Another method is to use a 1-inch wood bit and drill out the entire opening. Place the bit so each round corner is on the outline. After drilling four holes in a row on both sides, the center can be broken out with a screwdriver or wood chisel. Square each corner with a small hand or coping saw. Make sure the PCB and components fit inside and cover the rectangular hole.

Sand down all sides with a bench or power sander. If not available, sand down with a sandpaper block. Remove all dents and scratches. Sand the wood in a lengthwise direction. Spray on two or three coats of varnish, lacquer or clear finish. Let it thoroughly dry between coats, and smooth it with steel wool each time. Screw on the PCB, install the knobs and enjoy. Apply a coat of wax for a nice shine. It looks great!

Testing the circuit

Make sure the small AM radio is operating before it is mounted into the 2-×-4-inch cabinet. Plug in a pair of low-impedance headphones. Headphones with 16 to 40 ohms work best. If a pair of low-impedance stereo phones are used, install a stereo head-phone jack and connect both terminals together. Use a mono jack with a 2000-ohm pair of headphones (Fig. 3-8).

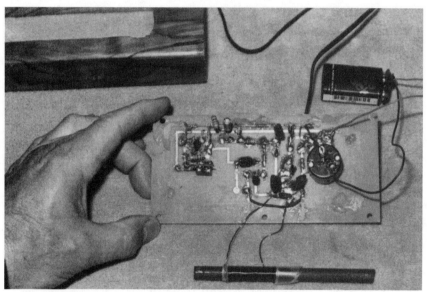

Fig. 3-8 *Plug in a pair of headphones and try out your radio.*

Rotate R2 to the ON position. Keep turning the control until a station is heard. Turn the PCB until the station comes in loudly. In fact, the only way to control the volume is by turning the PCB because there is no volume control. Although the small radio will pick up mostly local stations, high-powered stations can be heard 100 miles away. Rotate the radio for the best reception and volume.

If no audio is heard at all, measure the current at once. Shut off the radio. Measure the current across switch SW1 on back of tuning control R2. Any measurement over 15 milliameters (mA) indicates a leaky component or improper mounting of components. This radio draws 12.2 mA. Double check each terminal of VD1, IC1 and Q1. Make sure they are on the right PC wiring terminal.

Project 2: The breadboard AM radio

What you will need

IC1	ZN414 IC (DC Electronics, ZN414 or Circuit Specialists, ZN414)
IC2	LM386 power output IC
L2	77 turns of #24 or #26 enameled wire (see text)
L1	15 turns of #24 or #26 enameled wire (see text). All coils wound on ferrite rod
C1	365-pF variable capacitor (Antique Electronics Supply, CV-240 or KA7Q7Y Components, 365-pFvariable capacitor)
Ferrite rod	¼ to ⅜ inch diameter, 4 or 5 inches long (Antique Supply, PC-185 or Amidon, R61-050-400)
C2	0.01-µF, 50-volt ceramic capacitor
C3	0.1-µF, 50-volt ceramic capacitor
C4 & C5	10-µF, 35-volt electrolytic capacitor
C6 & C7	220-µF, 35-volt electrolytic capacitor
C8	0.05-µF, 50-volt ceramic capacitor
R1	100-kilohm, ½-watt resistor
R2	1-kilohm variable trimmer (screwdriver type)
R3	10-kilohm variable audio taper resistor with switch (SW1)
R4	10-ohm, ½-watt resistor
J1	Stereo headphone jack
B1, B2	Two 1.5-volt penlight cells
SW1	Double-pole, single-throw toggle switch (DPST)
Breadboard	270 connection joints or less (Radio Shack, 276-175)
Misc.	Hookup wire, jumper wire, solder, etc.

You can build a breadboard radio in one sitting by plugging parts into a solderless breadboard chassis. A low-priced IC breadboard can be used with less than 270 connections. Just plug in the components at the right places and connect with the jumper wires. If you like the way the small radio performs, place it on a perfboard or multipurpose board permanently. Then choose your own cabinet or container (Fig. 3-9).

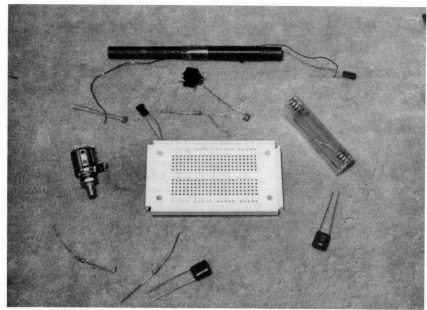

Fig. 3-9 *You can build this receiver in one evening simply by plugging all the parts into a solderless breadboard.*

How the circuit works

The single antenna coil (L2) is tuned by capacitor C1 and fed to input terminal 2 of IC1 (ZN414) (Fig. 3-10). L1 can be added if an outside antenna needs to be connected. Many stations can be pulled in with no outside antenna. IC1 is a Ferranti linear integrated circuit packaged in a 3-pin TO-18 transistor package for simplicity and space economy. The RF IC provides a complete RF amplifier, detector, and AGC circuit and requires only a few components. No IC sockets are needed with this radio. The rectified RF signal at pin 1 feeds directly to a volume control (R3). C4 couples the audio to pin 3 of IC2. The power IC (LM386, Fig. 3-11) provides easy listening for the stereo headphone jack (J1). This little radio is powered with two penlight batteries. The RF IC receives 1.5 volts from the power pack.

Winding the coils

Roll on 77 turns of #24 or 26 enameled wire on a ferrite rod. These rods can be purchased through mail-order catalogs or taken from

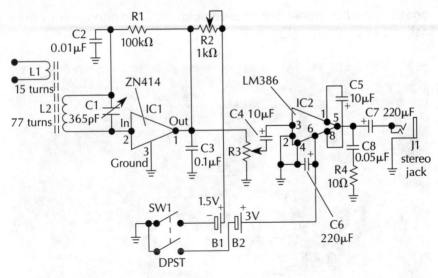

Fig. 3-10   *This schematic diagram shows two IC components powered with two penlight cells.*

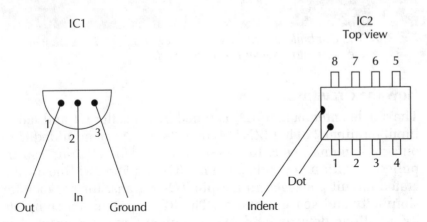

Fig. 3-11   *The bottom and top terminal leads of IC1 and IC2.*

old discarded radios. Wind 15 turns of #24 or 26 enameled wire for L1 if an outside antenna is desired (Fig. 3-12).

You use tape over both ends of the coil to hold it in place. Coil dope or model plastic cement can be added later. Clean off all enamel coating from the wire and tin the wire with solder. Be sure you have a good clean connection for inserting the clips. You can double the wire over in the breadboard so it will make a better connection, or solder the coil wires to the breadboard wire

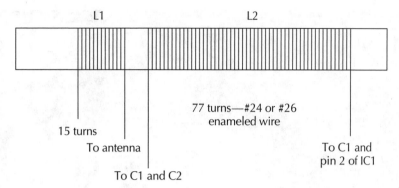

Fig. 3-12 *Wind 77 turns of #24 or #26 enameled wire on a ferrite form.*

for a good connection. Leave about 10 inches of lead on each wire so it can be tuned for better reception.

Wiring the circuit

Most breadboards take #22 to 24 wire leads for good connections. Instead of ¼ watt, use ½-watt resistors for larger wire. Connect three #22 solid hookup wires to the volume control. Solder two 6-inch leads of solid wire for J1. Likewise, solder hookup wire to the small battery holder. You can solder L2 and C1 together and use two wires to plug it into the breadboard.

Straddle IC2 at the bottom of the breadboard (Fig. 3-13). Usually contact points on a breadboard connect to both sides of a given pin. Small parts can be mounted by plugging them into the correct holes on the breadboard. Jumper wires are needed to connect the circuit together. You can purchase these wires at a supply or mail-order parts warehouse or make your own out of #22 hookup wire. Mount IC1 at the top of the breadboard.

Double check the wiring connections. Double check that each wire lead is plugged into a tight-fitting hole. Be careful when tying circuits together with jumper wires. Make sure you are connecting the wires to the right holes on the board. Connect the batteries to the board at the last minute. Switch SW2 may be eliminated by plugging the negative ground terminal of the batteries directly to the common ground terminal to turn the radio on.

Testing the circuit

Plug in the battery ground wire and the headphones. These headphones can be the stereo type used in portable tape players. The

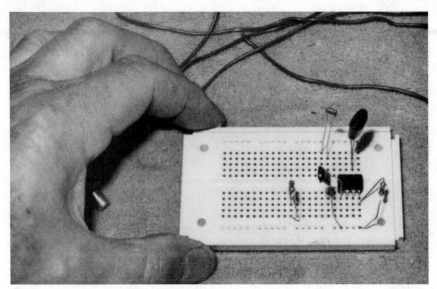

Fig. 3-13 *IC2 straddles the breadboard terminals at the bottom, and IC1 is mounted at the top of the breadboard.*

impedance output can range from 8 to 42 ohms (Fig. 3-14). They can also be picked up for less than $5.

You should hear a click in the earphones when the battery terminal is connected. Rotate the volume control (R3) half way. Turn the variable capacitor (C1) to tune in stations. You will be surprised at the selection of stations and the volume. By adding

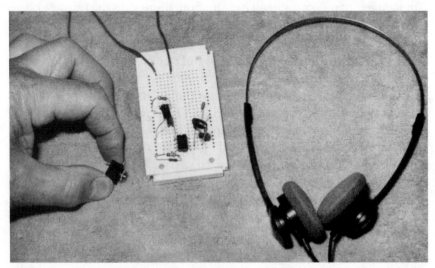

Fig. 3-14 *You can use an inexpensive pair of low-impedance headphones with this breadboard radio.*

one or two more penlight cells, the volume can be increased to operate a small speaker.

If you hear squealing around the broadcast stations, adjust R2 for clean reception and no distortion. Once R2 is adjusted, no further adjustment is needed. Why not transfer all the components to a PC board or a perfboard to make the radio permanent? Then install it into a small plastic case or regular cabinet. Besides, you may want to use the same breadboard to build additional projects.

Project 3: The integrated AM radio

What you will need

IC1	ZN414 RF IC (DC Electronics, ZN414 or Circuit Specialists, ZN414)
Q1	1S4 pentode power amplifier tube
C1	365-pF variable capacitor (Antique Supply, CF-230 or KA7QJY Components 365 pF)
C2 & C4	0.01-µF, 50-volt ceramic capacitor
C3	0.1-µF, 50-volt ceramic capacitor
L1	77 turns of 24 or 26 enameled wire over ferrite rod
R1	100-kilohm, ½-watt resistor
R2	1-kilohm, ½-watt resistor
R3	50-kilohm audio taper with switch on back
R4	470-kilohm, ½-watt resistor
J1	Headphone jack or post
SW1	Double-pole, single-throw toggle switch (DPST)
PC board	2 × 4 inch, cut from larger piece of PC board
B1	1.5-volt battery D cell
Battery holder	RS270-386A (holds 2 D batteries)
B2	2 9-volt batteries in series
Tube socket	7-pin PC mount (Antique Electronics Supply, PS-201)
Misc.	2-×-4-inch piece of PCB, bolts and nuts, solder, etc.

Back in the early days of radio, all radios, except crystal sets, were designed around the vacuum tube. Radio tubes were found in the one-tube AM radio, FM radio, regeneration radio, amplifiers, and superhet circuits. Most of these radios operated from batteries, although ac circuits were found in the later models. This radio project uses an RF IC component with one tube as amplifier (Fig. 3-15).

Fig. 3-15 *The integrated radio combines a tube amplifier with a sensitive, solid-state RF device.*

How the circuit works

IC1 is an RF, detector circuit, AGC, and amplifier, all found inside a transistor-type case. The RF amplifier has several high-gain RF stages. Effective AGC action is adjusted by selecting one external resistor value. Excellent audio quality can be had with very little current consumption. In fact, IC1 operates from 1.5 volts (Fig. 3-16).

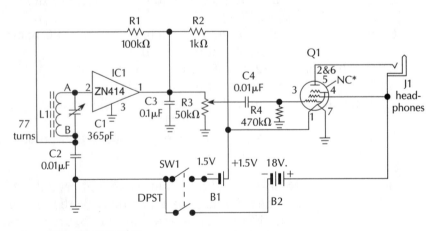

*NC=No connection

Fig. 3-16 *The RF IC operates from the same 1.5-volt source as is used by the filament of the IS4 battery-operated tube.*

The audio signal from pin 1 of IC1 connects directly to the volume control (R3) and to pin 3 of Q1. The 1S4 tube (Q1) serves as an audio amplifier. Since it is a low-filament voltage variety tube, the tube needs only 1.5 volts, the same voltage source that feeds IC1. The power pentode filament voltage is 1.4 volts at 0.05 amps. Pins 1 and 7 are the filament terminals.

C1 couples the audio signal from R3 to pin 3 of Q1. Pins 4 and 6 operate from a higher voltage source. Although the 1S4 was designed to operate from either 45 or 90 volts, lower plate and screen voltage is found in the integrated radio. With a plate voltage of 45 volts, the plate current is only 3.8 milliamperes. The radio pulls a total of 2.5 milliamperes of current from the B battery. Greater audio can be obtained by adding another 9-volt battery or up to 45 volts.

Winding the coil

Wind on 77 turns of #24 or #26 enameled wire on a ¼- or ⅜-inch ferrite rod. Coil L1 is turned by capacitor C1. Plenty of stations can be heard with only one RF coil. Place 15 turns on another winding, ⅛ inch away from the end of pin 1 (IC1) if more stations are needed.

Start winding the coil by placing a strip of tape over the wire and core to hold the wire and prevent it from unraveling. Secure both ends with tape after the coil is wound. This coil can be wound in 5 minutes. Secure the ends with coil dope or model cement to hold the winding permanently. The antenna should be mounted at least 3 inches from IC1. The coil can be held into position with a dash of rubber silicone cement at each end.

If, for instance, a local station at 550 kHz can't be heard, add more turns of coil wire. If the station a 550 kHz is ⅓ of the way with C1 open, remove turns from coil until the station can be heard where the variable capacitor plates are almost meshed. Rotate the wood chassis to increase reception on weak stations.

Laying out the PC board

Cut a 2-x-4-inch piece of PCB from a larger piece for wiring the entire circuit. Lay out the wiring as shown in Fig. 3-17. The entire board can be etched in 37 minutes. Make sure all dot connections are pressed tight on the copper side. Leave room for four bolt mounting holes at each corner.

Inspect the entire board after it is etched. Make certain all tie

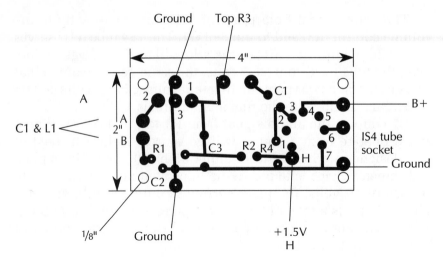

Fig. 3-17 *Layout of the PC board can be completed within one or two hours.*

wires are in place. When a board is etched too long, some of the wire connections are etched through. Check each one with the low-ohm scale of the ohmmeter, if in doubt. Bridge any gaps with regular tinned hookup wire.

Drill out all holes with a PCB bit or the smallest bit available. Drill out the 7-pin tube socket holes with ³⁄₃₂-inch bit. Slip the PCB socket into position and see how it fits. Each corner hole can be drilled with a ⁵⁄₃₂-inch bit. These holes are critical for correct seating.

Mounting parts

First, mount all small resistor and capacitor components. Solder each hole as the parts are mounted. Solder around the tube pins after bending over the small prongs. If the socket pins are not tinned or they are corroded, clean up and apply solder paste before mounting the socket.

When soldering extension wires to J1, B+ and negative leads, and to the volume control, mark each lead at the end with tape. This only takes a minute, but saves a lot of time in the long run. Solder in the RF IC last. Use long-nose pliers on each lead as a heat sink. Too much heat may destroy the small IC components. Tie in all wires to the outside mounted parts (Fig. 3-18).

Building the chassis

The radio can be mounted inside a plastic or wood box. Here, the small radio is mounted on a piece of wood. Drill the required

Fig. 3-18 *Soldering one of the last components to the integrated radio circuit.*

holes. Cut a piece of wood 6 × 10 inches (Fig. 3-19). Clean off all dirt and sand wooden areas. Spray on two or three coats of clear acrylic or lacquer, sanding between coats to keep the wood clean and the surface unmarred.

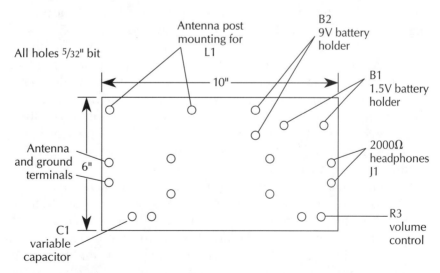

Fig. 3-19 *Place the finished radio in a plastic box or mount it on a wood chassis.*

Connecting the batteries

Two D cells are connected in parallel, with one battery reversed (B1) from the other. Instead of the spring being at the negative terminal, reverse one battery so the positive end points the same way. By using two D cells in parallel, the batteries will last longer. Solder a hookup wire to the solid bar at the rear, or at the brass rivets. Be careful not to melt the black plastic case. Then connect both red and black wires together for the positive lead. This lead will go to pin 1 of Q1.

Connect the two 9-volt batteries in series. One black wire (negative) connects to the common filament and the pin 1 terminal, while the red lead goes to the black lead of the next 9-volt battery. The remaining red lead (18 V) connects to one of the headphone posts and pin 4 of Q1. If the radio is used extensively, both batteries (B1 and B2) can be substituted with the rechargeable nickel-cadmium types. The 9-volt batteries last longer since only 2.5 mA of current drain is measured.

For the low-impedance output of Q1, instead of J1, connect a 1-kilohm to 2.5-kilohm audio output transformer with an 8-ohm secondary. Place the jack at the 8-ohm output winding for low-impedance headphones.

Testing the circuit

Double check the wiring of the 1.5-volt battery. If higher voltage than 1.5 volts is applied to the filament of the tube, the filament will burn out. Make sure the B+ supply is tied to pin 4 and to the headphone jack, and 1.5 volts is applied to pin 1 and grounded to pin 7.

Rotate the volume control halfway open. Make sure the headphones are plugged in, then slowly rotate C1. Stations along the dial should be heard. If not, rotate the volume control wide open. Check to see if the filament in the tube is lit. Measure the voltage on all tube terminals. Touch the center terminal of the volume control with a screwdriver blade. A click or low hum should be heard.

If the audio stage seems normal, check the voltage on the IC1 terminals. Compare all voltages with those on the schematic. Make sure IC1 terminals are soldered correctly on the PC board. With one side of C1 and L1 disconnected from the PC board, you should hear noise when they are touched with a screwdriver blade. Correct voltage and resistance tests should uncover any problems.

From building the integrated AM receiver, you can learn how to connect tubes and solid-state devices together. You learn how the tube amplifier works, why it requires two different voltage sources, and how other tube circuits work in Chapter 4.

Project 4: The three-IC AM radio

What you will need

IC1	ZN414 IC (DC Electronics, ZN414 or Circuit Specialists, ZN414)
IC2	741 operational amplifier (op amp)
IC3	LM386 power output amplifier
C1	365-pF variable capacitors (Antique Supply, CV-230)
C2	0.01-µF, 100-volt ceramic capacitor
C3, C4, C6, & C7	0.1-µF ceramic capacitor
C5	47-µF, 35-volt electrolytic capacitor
C8 & C10	220-µF, electrolytic capacitor
C9	10-µF, 35-volt electrolytic capacitor
C11	0.05-µF, 100-volt ceramic capacitor
L1	77 turns of #26 enameled wire on ⅜-inch ferrite rod
R1	100-kilohm, ½-watt resistor
R2	1-kilohm trimmer variable resistor
R3 & R4	2.2-kilohm, ½-watt resistor
R5 & R8	1-kilohm, ½-watt resistor
R6	47-kilohm, ½-watt resistor
R7	10-kilohm audio taper control
R9	10-ohm, ½-watt resistor
R10	1-kilohn, ½-watt resister
2	IC 8-pin sockets
Spk.	4- or 5-inch, 8-ohm PM speakers
2	2-cell C battery holders
1	1-cell C battery holder
B1	Four, 1.5-V C batteries
SW1	Double-pole, single-throw switch (DPST)
Misc.	Wood chassis, masonite panel, screws, hookup wire, piece of perfboard, solder, etc.

The three-IC radio is a powerful little radio loaded with AM stations that can easily drive a 5-inch speaker. Only an RF IC and two IC audio components are needed to provide plenty of volume and selectivity. The RF component (ZN414) is a tuned RF circuit, detector circuit, and amplifier in one transistor-type package. Both audio ICs plug into 8-pin IC sockets. All small components are mounted on a perfboard (Fig. 3-20).

Fig. 3-20   *The three IC AM radio in operation. This radio has plenty of volume to drive a 4- or 5-inch speaker.*

How the circuit works

The RF IC (IC1) has a single variable capacitor (C1) and coil (L1) attached to the input terminal (2). Terminal 3 is grounded. Output terminal 1 is capacitance-coupled to the first audio IC (IC2) stage. The RF IC is powered with one of the batteries (1.5 V) in the battery pack (Fig. 3-21).

IC2 (741) amplifies the weak audio signal at input terminal (2), with the output connected directly to the volume control (R7). R7 controls the audio volume applied to input terminal 3 of IC3 (LM386). Output terminal 5 of IC3 is coupled to the speaker with capacitor C10. IC2 and IC3 are powered with a 6-volt power source and IC3 adequately drives a 4- or 5-inch, 8-ohm speaker, with plenty of volume to spare.

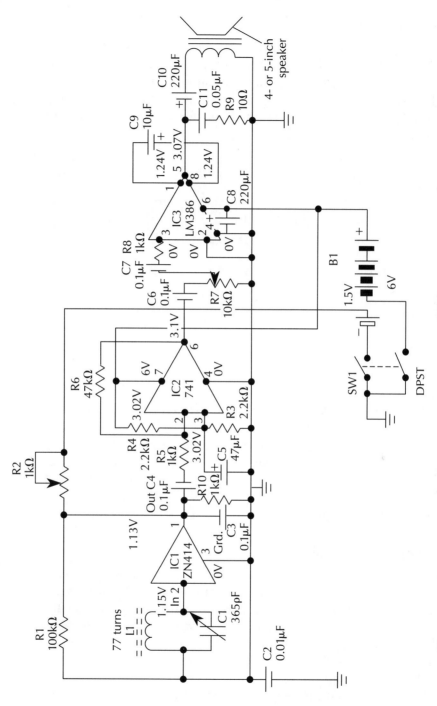

Fig. 3-21   The three-IC AM radio circuit contains one RF circuit, first audio stage, and audio output ICs.

Winding the coil

The antenna coil can be wound on ¼- or ⅜-inch-diameter ferrite rod. Wind 77 turns of #26 enameled wire directly on the iron core. Loop a small piece of tape over the wire, fold the end and lay the tape on the core form. Wind the coil right over the tape to prevent the wire from unraveling. This coil is close-wound and can be done in 5 minutes (Fig. 3-22).

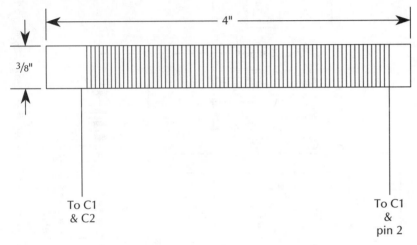

Fig. 3-22 *Wind on 77 turns of #26 enameled wire on a ⅜-inch ferrite rod.*

Fasten the end of the coil with a small piece of tape. Place a drop of coil dope, plastic model, or rubber silicone cement over the coil ends. After the coil dope dries, remove the tape. Leave 6 inches of extra wire at each end of the coil for mounting. Lay the coil aside while mounting parts on the perfboard.

Preparing the perfboard

Cut a 2-×-3-inch piece of perfboard. Mount the audio IC sockets away from IC1. Where the parts are mounted on the board is not too critical, as long as the RF circuits are kept away from the audio output circuits. Keep all leads as short as possible. Usually, perfboard wiring does not have as neat an appearance as a PCB. The advantage of perfboard is it's a quick method of wiring components together (Fig. 3-23).

When placing connecting lead wires from the perfboard to existing components, mark the ends with tape and mark where each are connected. The speaker, volume control, tuning capacitor, antenna coil, and battery leads must be connected to the perf-

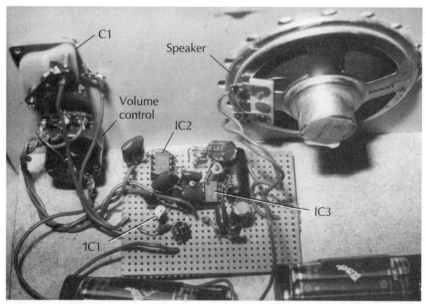

Fig. 3-23 *Closeup view of how the small parts are mounted on the perfboard.*

board circuits. All connecting wires should be fed through the small holes from the top and soldered underneath so they do not pull out (Fig 3-24).

Fig. 3-24 *Soldering all wire connections from the PC board to various panel components.*

Be careful when soldering the small IC socket pins. Bend each one over flat. Use a sharp-pointed soldering iron tip to reach each terminal. Small hookup wire and solder helps. Do not let too much solder collect on the soldering iron point as it may run over into another connection. Test each socket connection for a good solder bond by lifting the joint wire with a pocketknife. Clean out all solder tips and wire pieces between the IC pins. Cross off with x marks each connection as it is soldered.

Check the wiring at least twice so that no parts are incorrectly soldered together. Check continuity with the low-ohm range of an ohmmeter from each component to each IC terminal for solid solder connections. Apply the probe on top of the corresponding pin and check the continuity to the corresponding component under and on top of the chassis.

Connecting the batteries

The 4 C batteries are wired in series and can be mounted in one holder or in two different holders. The 1.5-volt tap for IC1 is easily soldered to the one battery cell of a 2-cell battery holder (Fig. 3-25). Tap the first battery voltage at the ground end. The negative terminal of the batteries are connected to SW1.

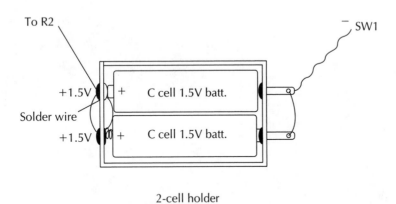

Fig. 3-25 *The 1.5-volt battery connection. Start with the ground for the first battery wire tap.*

A 4-cell battery holder can be used if a metal insert is placed between the first and second battery. Cut a piece of brass or copper with terminal wire and insert it between the first and second battery. This 1.5-volt lead solders directly to one end of R2. By placing SW1 in series with the negative lead, all batteries are switched into or out of the power circuits.

Building the chassis

The small perfboard and components are mounted on an L-type chassis. Cut a piece of masonite or plastic 5 × 8 inches for the front panel. Saw a piece of soft pine or pressed board 4½ × 7¼ inches. Drill holes in the front panel for the speaker, volume control, and variable capacitor. Drill three ⅛-inch holes at the bottom to hold the front panel to the rear chassis (Fig. 3-26).

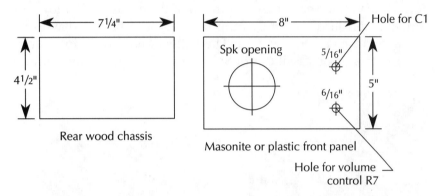

Fig. 3-26   *The chassis and front panel layout with hole dimensions.*

Spray front panel with two coats of car enamel paint. The rear chassis may be left unpainted, or a coat of clear acrylic spray may be used.

Mount the speaker, variable capacitor, and volume control on the front panel. Leave R7 terminals up for easy soldering. Place the perfboard between the volume control and the speaker. Screw the battery holders at the rear-center of the chassis board. The perfboard may be bolted or held to the wood chassis with rubber silicone cement.

Testing the circuit

After all the connections are made, insert the IC components and batteries. Make sure the IC dots line up with terminal 1 on the IC sockets. Double check that all IC pins are in the socket and not folded up or outside the socket terminals. Check each battery for correct polarity.

When the volume is tuned up you should hear a full band of

stations. If any whistling or squealing is heard when the stations are tuned in, adjust R2.

If the radio will not perform, double check all wiring. Take voltage measurements on the ICs and compare to the schematic. Insert a current meter between the last C cell and the terminal. Hold the cell away from the connection with a slip of paper or thin cardboard. This radio pulls only 12 to 14.5 milliamps (mA) of current with a station tuned in. Suspect a poor or crossed connection, an IC mounted in the socket backwards, or a poorly soldered connection, if the current measurement is over 20 mA.

You should hear a small click when the test probe touches the top of the volume control or at pin 2 of IC2 (Fig. 3-27). Remove one antenna coil lead, and a rushing noise should be heard with the volume turned all the way up. The battery should last for months with such a low current drain. So, sit back and enjoy your radio!

Fig. 3-27 *To test the audio output stage, touch the volume control with a screwdriver blade and listen for a click in the speaker. Even though the click may be very low, it indicates IC3 is working.*

Project 5: The solar IC AM radio

What you will need

IC1   ZN414 IC (DC Electronics ZN414 or
                Circuit Specialists, ZN414)

IC2	LM386 IC
C1	365-pF variable capacitor (Antique Electronics Supply, CV-230 or KA7QJY Components, 365 pF)
C2	0.01-μF ceramic, 100-V capacitor
C3 & C4	0.1-μF ceramic, 100-V capacitor
C5 & C6	10-μF, 35-V electrolytic capacitor
C7 & C8	220-μF, 35-V electrolytic capacitor
C9	0.05-μF, 100-V ceramic capacitor
L1	77 turns of #24 or #26 enameled wire on ferrite rod
L2	25 turns of #24 or #26 enameled wire on ferrite rod
R1	100-kilohm, ½-watt resistor
R2	1-kilohm screwdriver adjustment resistor (Radio Shack, 271-227)
R3	10-kilohm audio taper control
R4	10 Ω ½-watt resistor
J1	Stereo 3.5-millimeter audio jack (Radio Shack, 274-249A)
9	Solar cells (at least 50 mA) (Edmund Scientific Co., 537, 337 or 535; or H & R Co., TM39SED5715—200 mA solar cells cut in two)
PC board	Multi-purpose PCB (RS, 276-150)
SW1	Single-pole, single-throw switch on rear of R3
Misc.	Cabinet, solder, hookup wire, nuts and bolts, etc.

The solar radio operates under sunlight or a lamp. This means the radio does not pull too much current, but still provides excellent radio reception. This is practically the same circuit as in the linear IC radio, except from solar cells instead of batteries (Fig. 3-28). Also, IC2 is used instead of transistors.

How the circuit works

On the radio schematic (Fig. 3-28) you see two IC components, ZN414 as the circuit RF, detector circuit, and amplifier. The output amp uses the familiar LM386 IC chip. Since IC1 operates at less than 1.5 volts, the solar cells are tapped at the third solar cell. The total voltage from the solar bank to IC2 is about 4.5 volts. This dc voltage can be increased by adding more solar cells in series.

The RF signal is picked up by antenna coil L1 and tuned with a 365-pF variable capacitor (C1). The tuned RF signal is fed into input terminal 2 of IC1. The RF signal is amplified and rectified,

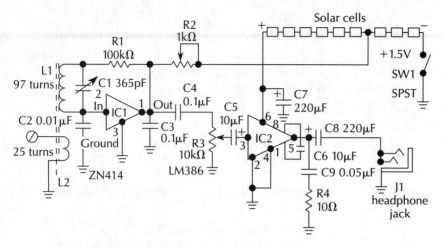

Fig. 3-28 *This wiring schematic shows that L1 and C1 tune in stations if powered by 9 small pieces of solar cells.*

and the audio signal is heard at output pin 1. Capacitor C4 couples the audio signal to the volume control (R3). R3 also turns on switch SW1.

Capacitor C5 couples the audio signal to input terminal 3 of IC2. The amplified output signal is coupled from pin 5, through C8, and to stereo headphone jack J1. A low-impedance (8 to 42 ohms) stereo headphone can be used. Positive 4.5 dc volts are fed to pin 6 from the solar panel.

Winding the coil

Wind 77 turns of #24 or 26 enameled wire over a ⅜-or ½-inch ferrite rod. If an outside antenna is to be connected to receive additional stations, wrap 25 turns of #24 or 26 enameled wire ⅛ inch from L1. Local radio stations can be picked up without an outside antenna (Fig. 3-29).

Secure both ends of the coil with tape so that it will not unravel. Place a drop of plastic model or coil cement over the end windings. After the cement sets, remove the tape from the ends. Coil L1 is tuned using capacitor C1 for the broadcast band.

Constructing the solar cell

Choose nine solar cell pieces to supply at least a load of 50 milliamperes. These can be ½- or ¾-inch-square pieces. Sometimes, broken pieces of solar cells can be purchased separately. If you cannot find those, 250-milliampere cells can be cut. Solar cells

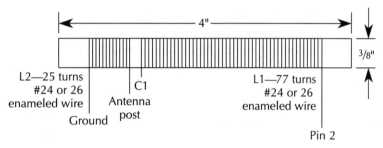

Fig. 3-29 *Wind on 77 turns of #24 or #26 enameled wire for L1, and 25 turns for L2 if an outside antenna is needed. If you want to pick up distant stations, you will need L2.*

can be broken by creasing the back with sharp knife and ruler. Then break the cells over a sharp edge of wood.

Connect the solar cells in series to get the required voltage (Fig. 3-30). Extra care must be exercised at this point. Use fine hookup wire and do not leave the iron on the soldered joint too long. Solder one lead to the back of the cell (the positive terminal) and the other lead to the top (the negative terminal). Try to locate a large vane on the top side. When all cells are wired in series you should have approximately 4.5 volts under sunlight. Tap off a lead at the positive terminal of the third cell from the negative lead of ZN414.

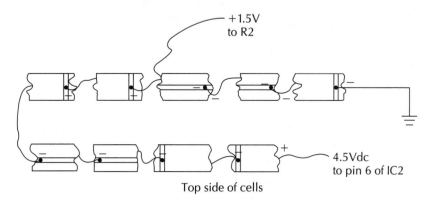

Fig. 3-30 *Connect the solar cells in series and be very careful when soldering to the top cell.*

Place the wired series of cells under a 100-watt lamp and test the voltage of each cell. A low voltage can indicate a poorly soldered connection. Under sunlight, the total voltage of the cells should measure approximately 4.5 volts dc.

After the cells are wired together and tested, place them on the back of a piece of PC board or, if the radio is to be built inside a plastic cabinet, place them right on the plastic top (Fig. 3-31). Cement the cells to the plastic with model or rubber silicone cement. The cells can be put in a line or in a group. The cells can be protected with a coat of clear varnish or a thin piece of plastic. Solar cells can be purchased from mail-order electronic stores at lower prices.

Fig. 3-31 *Place solar cells on the back of the PC board, or on top of a plastic cabinet.*

Testing the circuit

Place the top of the radio in sunlight or under at least a 100-watt light bulb. Rotate the volume control R3 for its loudest setting. Rotate tuning capacitor (C1) until you hear a broadcast station. Adjust R2 (AGC) until the station is at its loudest without any distortion. Tune R2 on all available stations, especially the highest-powered one in your area. Mount the antenna rod at least 3 or 4 inches from the chassis to prevent feedback. This radio will provide happy listening for years, and you don't have to worry about changing batteries!

❖4

Regenerative receiver projects

DR. EDWIN ARMSTRONG INVENTED THE SUPERHET AND THE regenerative radio receiver circuits. The regenerative radio receiver has terrific gain and selectivity, and uses only a few electronic parts, and has been around since Grandpa built his first shortwave receiver in the 1920s and 1930s. Regenerative radios have opened up a new era for the radio amateur.

The early regenerative radio was powered with batteries, but later operated from an ac power line. Although, the early regenerative receiver consisted of only one tube and covered only the broadcast band, the two-tube receiver became popular for listening to the 80-, 40-, 20- and 5-meter amateur bands.

The two-tube regenerative receiver consisted of two battery-operated tubes, a tuning coil, a variable capacitor, an interstage transformer, and a pair of headphones. The regenerative detector has a tickler coil in the plate circuit of the variable capacitor, which feeds the signal back to the original grid coil, producing long-distance reception. Usually another tuning capacitor or a variable resistor determined the point of regeneration.

When a loud whistling noise was heard when tuning the variable capacitor, the regeneration control was reduced until audio was heard. Of course there is a very fine line between oscillation and actual audio when tuning in a frequency. Slight readjustment of the regeneration and tuning controls can bring in good audio reception. When trying to tune in a weak, distant station, fine tuning of the regeneration and control circuits must be made several times.

The regenerative receiver can cause oscillation in other radio devices within its range. An RF stage ahead of the regenerative detector helps prevent this strong signal radiation. It is best to tune in the regenerative receiver using a pair of headphones to prevent squealing and whistling noises that can be heard in a speaker. These noises can be annoying to other people in the house.

The regenerative radio is fun to build and listen to. For just a few dollars you can tune in London, France, and Italy on the shortwave band without any difficulty. Central and South American stations also come in without any problem. So let's build a few regenerative radios and listen!

Project 1: The regenerative AM tube radio

What you will need

Q1	1S4 7-pin vacuum tube (Antique Electronics Supply or Radio Shack)
C1	90-pF trimmer capacitor (DC Electronics, 24AA067 or Antique Electronics Supply, CV-421)
C2	365-pF variable capacitor (Antique Electronics Supply, CV-230, or KA7QJY Components, 365 pF)
L1	108 turns, #24 or #26 enameled wire (see text)
L2	15 turns, #24 or #26 enameled wire (see text)
C3, C4	270-pF silver mica capacitor
C5	0.1-μF, 50-volt ceramic capacitor
R1	2.2-megohm, ½-watt resistor
R2	50-kilohm linear variable control
SW1	Flexible wire and alligator clip
SW2	Single-pole, single-throw (SPST) toggle switch on rear of R2
RFC	RF choke coil, 2.5 mh (Antique Electronics Supply, PC 1535B or KA7QJY Components, Supply 2.5 mH)
J1	Push-button speaker terminals (Radio Shack, 274-315)
Metal panel	3-×-5¾-inch anodized aluminum (All Electronics, PNL-3)
B1	Two 1.5-volt C cells, wired in parallel
B2	Three 9-volt batteries, wired in series.
Tube socket	7-pin wafer (Antique Electronics, PS-201)
Misc.	C-cell battery holder, three 9-volt wire terminals and leads, knobs, screws, hookup wire, solder, plastic ½-inch spacers, etc.

The most simple, high-gain AM radio can be constructed using a 1S4 tube. This regenerative radio requires a pair of 2000-ohm headphones attached to the outside amp. It also requires an outside antenna and ground for good reception (Fig. 4-1).

Fig. 4-1   *This small regenerative AM-tube radio is built on a wood chassis and a metal front panel.*

How the circuit works

The radio signal is picked up from the antenna, through a trimmer capacitor (C1) and to coil L1 (Fig. 4-2). The coil taps are tuned and connected into the circuit with an alligator clip. Variable capacitor C2 tunes in the AM broadcast station. The regenerative detector (1S4) plate coil (L2) feeds back part of the received signal, and is heard with a pair of high-impedance headphones.

Regeneration is controlled by variable resistor R2. When a loud whistle or squeal is heard in the headphones, reduce R2 until only audio is heard. Several adjustments may be needed for weak AM stations. A slight adjustment of capacitor C2 may be needed to bring in distant stations. Adjustment of C1 helps tune the antenna to separate strong local stations.

Filament voltage from two D-cell batteries (B1) connected in parallel are applied to pins 1 and 7 of Q1. B2 totals three 9-volt batteries connected in series to provide B+ plate and regeneration voltage. J1 connects the audio to a pair of 2000-ohm headphones.

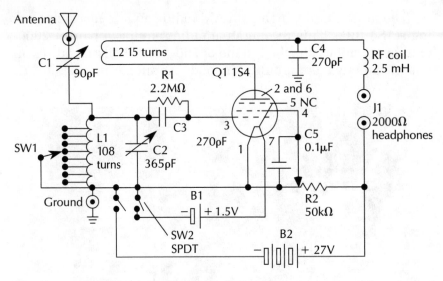

Fig. 4-2 *Only about a dozen parts are found in the regenerative receiver circuit.*

Winding the coils

The 1½-inch-diameter coil form can be PVC plastic pipe or plumbing drain fixtures. L1 is wound close over an area of approximately 2½ inches. Drill a ¹⁄₁₆-inch hole to start the coil and also at the finish (Fig. 4-3).

Using #24 enameled wire, wind on a total of 108 turns for coil L1 on the PVC plastic pipe about 3¼ inches long and about ½ inch in diameter (Fig. 4-4). Then make the first tap. Leave one inch of

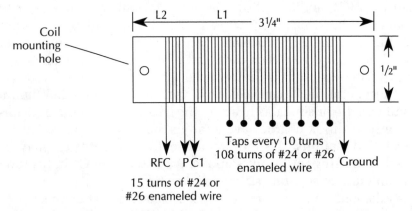

Fig. 4-3 *Wind both coils on PVC pipe using either #24 or #26 enameled wire. For coil L1, wind 108 turns on the pipe, and tap every 10 turns.*

Fig. 4-4 *The completed coil with the windings secured with plastic model cement.*

wire stuck out from the form, and twist the loop at least six times. Wind on another 10 turns of wire for the second tap. Continue this process until 9 taps and a total of 108 turns are wound on the coil form. Try to keep the taps in line.

Scrape each coil tap to remove the enameled coating from the wire. Use either solder paste or extra heat on each tap before soldering to provide a good solder connection. A poorly soldered tap may result in an open coil winding, so check the winding with a low ohmmeter range.

Space L2 ⅛ inch away from L1. Wind the coil in the same direction. Wind on 15 turns of #24 or 26 enameled wire. Leave about 4 inches to make connections. Secure both ends of each coil with coil dope, plastic cement, or rubber silicone cement. Let dry for a couple of hours.

Double check the winding with an ohmmeter. If you get no reading, check each tap until the faulty one is found. Resolder the tap and test again with the ohmmeter.

Solder a piece of flexible hookup wire to the ground side. Attach a small alligator clip to the other end. The alligator clip serves as a 9-position switch. Simply tune the coil to different bands by attaching the clip to a different tap. Make the flexible lead just long enough to reach the last tap. Bolt the coil to the wooden chassis. When soldering wires to different parts, place a piece of paper under the soldering area so you do not mark up the chassis.

Building the chassis

While the coils are drying, prepare the front panel and the rear chassis. For regenerative receivers, the front panel or cabinet should be made out of metal since stray capacitance may detune the circuits. Here a 3⅛-×-5¾-inch anodized piece of aluminum was used for the front panel. These panels can be ordered separately from a parts supplier and cost only about $1–$2.

The rear panel was cut from a 5½-×-5¼-inch piece of pine board. Any suitable piece of fir or cedar wood may be used. The front panel is screwed to the rear chassis with three small metal screws.

Before attaching the front panel, drill out all the required holes. Mount SW1 on the left side, and C1 on the right side. Drill ⁵⁄₁₆-inch holes on the panel for the regeneration control and switch (Fig. 4-5). Lay out holes on a sheet of paper and tape it to the front panel. Not only will this help locate holes, but it will protect the anodized surface from accidental scratches. Apply rub-on transfer numbers and letters before mounting any parts. Spray a coat of clear acrylic over the front panel for protection.

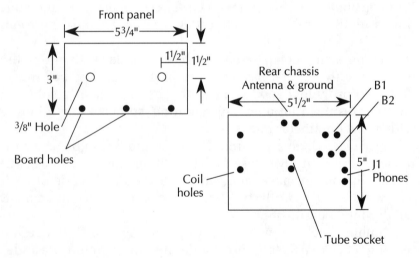

Fig. 4-5 *The front panel consists of a ¹⁄₁₆-inch piece of anodized aluminum.*

Mounting parts

Coil L1, batteries B1 and B2, jack J1, and the tube sockets are mounted on the wood chassis. Capacitor C2 and resistor R2 are mounted on the front panel. All small parts are tied to the circuit with terminal strips. First mount all large components. Then mount the smaller parts as you solder them into the circuit. Use the shortest route to connect all leads, especially coil and RF leads (Fig. 4-6). Face the filament pins towards rear of the chassis for easier connections.

Fig. 4-6 *Mount all parts on the chassis and front panel before connecting.*

Testing the circuit

Double check all wiring connections after the small radio is completely wired. Make sure the filament batteries (B1) and B2 batteries are wired correctly (Fig. 4-7). Remember to wire the two cells in parallel for 1.5 volts. The three 9-volt batteries (B2) are wired in series. Switch SW2 should be between both negative battery terminals of B1 and B2.

Plug in a pair of 2000-ohm impedance headphones. You can connect an external amplifier to the output if you use a matching driver transformer. Connect the primary of the driver transformer to headphone jack J1, and clip the amp to the secondary winding of the transformer (Fig. 4-8). Now, a low-impedance pair of headphones can be used with the regenerative receiver.

Rotate the regeneration control (R2) until a squeal is heard. No-

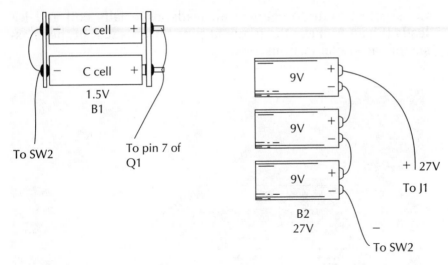

Fig. 4-7   *Connect the C cells in parallel and the 9-volt batteries in series.*

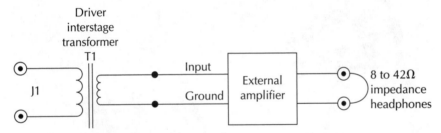

Fig. 4-8   *If you desire to connect the external audio amp to the receiver, place an interstage transformer between the headphone posts and the amp.*

tice how the stations whistle as variable capacitor C2 is rotated. Now slowly turn R2 until audio is heard. Each whistle you hear on the dial is a station. Move the alligator clip towards ground. You should pick up broadcast stations. When the alligator clip is moved towards the antenna, shortwave stations should start to come in.

If you do not hear a squeal or a whistle, reverse the secondary leads of coil L2 (Fig. 4-9). This provides signal feedback. Then again rotate R2 until you hear a whistle and tune in the strongest whistling station. Slowly decrease R2 until audio is heard. Several tries may be needed until you get the hang of how to operate the regenerative receiver (Fig. 4-10). Remember, each whistle is a station. If C1 is adjusted too tightly, regeneration may cease.

After tuning in a weak station, adjust C1 for maximum signal. Sometimes when C1 is adjusted, the tuning of C2 can be thrown off. Set C1 for the best signal on all bands.

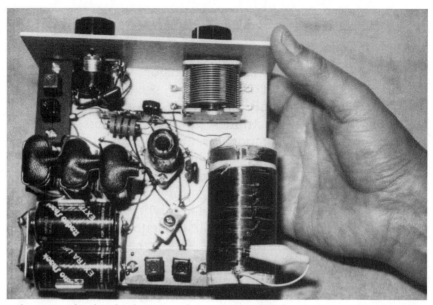

Fig. 4-9   *The finished unit ready to test. Run all leads as short as possible.*

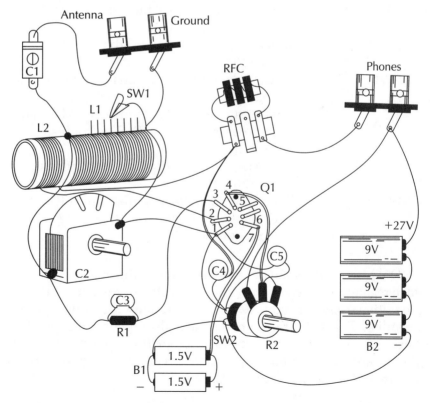

Fig. 4-10   *A pictorial diagram of the radio with all parts connected.*

Project 2: Two-stage regenerative radio

What you will need

Q1	FET MPF102 transistor
IC1	LM386 IC amp
C1	365-pF variable AM capacitor (Antique Electronics Supply, CV-230 or KA7QJY Components, 365 pF)
C2	270-pF, 50-V silver mica capacitor
C3	0.01-μF, 50-V ceramic capacitor
C4, C5, & C7	10-μF, 35-V electrolytic capacitor
C6, C9	220-μF, 35-V electrolytic capacitor
C8	0.05-μF ceramic capacitor
C10	0.001-μF, 50-V ceramic capacitor
L1	25 turns of #24 or #26 enameled wire)
L2	108 turns of #24 or #26 enameled wire, tapped at the 27th turn (see text)
R1	220-kilohm, ½-watt resistor
R2	1-kilohm, ½-watt resistor
R3, R4	10-kilohm linear variable control resistors
R5	10-ohm, ½-watt resistor
J1	Stereo headphone jack (Radio Shack, 276-148)
SW1	Single pole, single-throw switch on rear of R3
B1	9-V battery
T1	Driver transformer 10kΩ primary, 2kΩ secondary center-tapped (DC Electronics, 42K1002)
Cabinet	7¾-x-4⅜-x-2⅜-inch (Radio Shack, plastic box 270-232)
Misc.	Hookup wire, battery holder, 8-pin IC socket, bolts & nuts, solder, 5-inch ferrite round core, etc.

Only two solid-state devices are used in this small AM, two-stage regenerative receiver. Q1 is a field effect transistor (FET) regenerative detector and IC1 is the LM386 IC low-powered amplifier. The FET transistor has a high-impedance input like that of a triode vacuum tube. Although low-impedance headphones are recommended, powerful local stations may drive a four-inch PM speaker (Fig. 4-11).

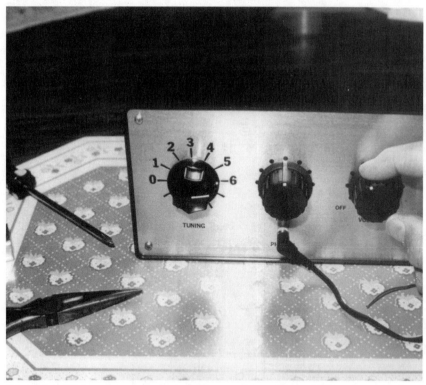

Fig. 4-11 *This two-stage regenerative receiver may be listened to with low-impedance headphones or a 4-inch PM speaker.*

How the circuit works

The outside antenna is connected to L1 within the high Q circuit of the secondary winding of L2. L1 consists of 25 turns of #24 or 26 enameled wire over the center of L2 (108 turns). L2 is tapped at the 27th turn and close wound on the ferrite rod. Variable capacitor C1 selects the tuned broadcast station, and the RF signal is fed to the gate terminal of Q1 through C2 (Fig. 4-12). Resistor R1 provides gate bias for the FET transistor (Q1).

Signal feedback occurs from the source terminal of Q1 to the tap on L2. There is no need to adjust the tickler coil in this regenerative receiver. Regeneration is controlled through the plate-load primary winding of transformer T1 by varying the voltage applied to the drain of Q1 (D) terminal.

The audio is transferred from the primary winding of T1 to the secondary winding, which is controlled by volume control R4 (10 kilohm). The controlled audio signal is coupled to pin 3

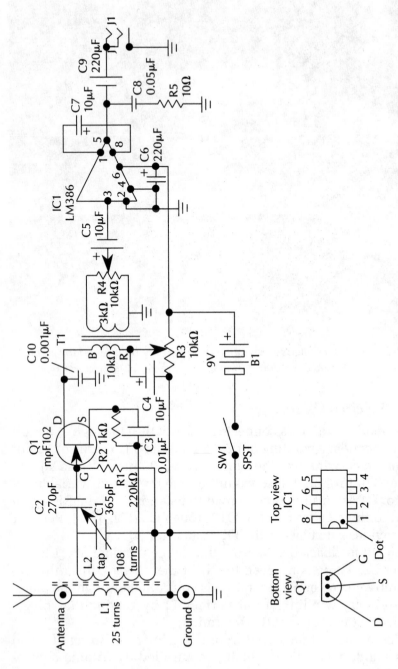

Fig. 4-12 *This regenerative circuit consists of an FET transistor and a feedback-tapped coil.*

of IC1 by capacitor C5. The audio output signal appears at pin 5 of IC1, and is coupled to headphone jack J1 with C9. IC1 supply voltage at pin 6 comes from a single 9-volt battery.

Building the PC board

Although this small regenerative two-stage receiver can be mounted on a multi-purpose PC board, the etched board works and looks much better. The layout of the PCB is not too critical, just be sure to separate the audio output from the regenerative detector circuits (Fig. 4-13).

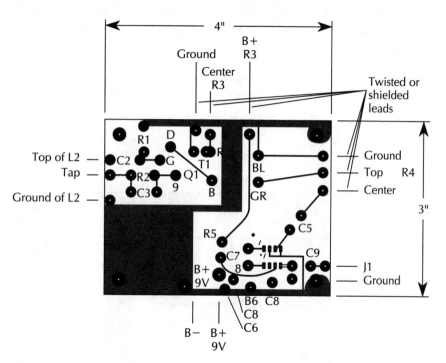

Fig. 4-13 *Layout of the PCB in this project is not critical except that it's important to keep the RF circuits away from the audio output.*

The etched board can be cut from a larger piece of PCB. Dry transfer dots and lines can be placed on the clean copper surface. The etching process takes only about 30 to 40 minutes to complete. Take a peek at the etching process after 15 minutes so you do not leave it in the solution too long and destroy the small copper lines.

Wash off the board in soapy water. Soapy steel wool pads are ideal to clean off etching material from the copper wiring. Now drill out those small component and mounting board holes. Double check to ensure all holes are drilled. If you discover some holes are missing after you have already mounted some of the parts, drilling is a little more difficult.

Winding the coils

Select a 4- or 5-inch-long ferrite rod to wind both coils on. First wind on L2, starting from ground. Wind on 27 turns of #24 or #26 enameled wire and twist the wire 7 times for a wire loop tap. Then continue to wind the remaining turns for a total of 108 turns (Fig. 4-14).

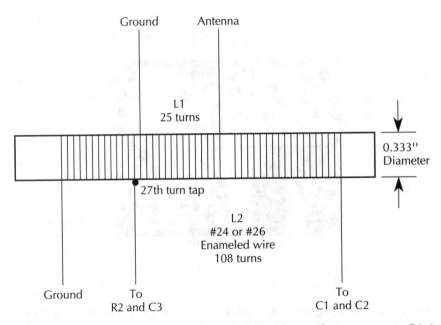

Fig. 4-14 *L2 has 108 turns with a tap at the 27th turn that connects to R2 & R4. L1 is wound on the top center of L2 with a total of 25 turns.*

Fasten each coil end with tape to hold the wires in place. Place the tape only where it can be removed. Now apply plastic cement or coil dope at each end. Let the cement set for an hour, and remove the tape for a better appearance.

Wind L1 over the center part of the coil. Stay on the large section of the winding, away from the 27th tap loop. Place a layer of tape over L1. Wind on 25 turns of #24 or #26 enameled wire. Secure the coil ends and apply coil dope or plastic cement. Always leave about 4 inches of wire to connect the coil to the RF circuits. The wire can be cut off as needed.

Mounting parts

Insert the leads of each component into the PC board. Solder each lead. Without using too much heat, make sure a good solder contact is made. A 30-watt or battery-operated iron is ideal for PCB soldering. Mount T1 by placing a drop of rubber silicone cement under the transformer. By mounting T1 last, the PC board can be set aside until the cement sets. When soldering in Q1, use long-nose pliers on each terminal as a heat sink.

All outside board components are tied to the PCB with flexible hookup wire. Keep all leads as short as possible. Notice that the 9-volt battery holder mounts on the PC board. SW1 can either be mounted on the rear of R3 or R4. Mount the PCB on the inside and bottom of the plastic cabinet.

Building the chassis

Choose a small plastic box with a metal aluminum cover for the cabinet enclosure. Lay out the front panel with the variable capacitor (C1), regeneration control (R3), and volume control (R4) mounted on the front panel. Mount the ferrite rod on the inside and top rear of the plastic cabinet (Fig. 4-15).

Before any parts are mounted on the front panel, drill all the required holes. Tape a piece of paper over the metal cover to prevent scratching the front piece, then drill all marked holes. After holes are drilled, apply transfer dials, decals, and numbers. Spray on a coat of clear acrylic to prevent damaging the numbers.

Testing the circuit

Before mounting the metal plate and the PC board, test the receiver. Connect the 9-volt battery, IC1, and headphones. Turn volume control R4 fully on. Slowly advance the regeneration control (R3) until the set goes into oscillation. Tune in a loud whistle or local station. Now slowly reduce R3 until a pleasant sound is heard.

If the radio fails to respond, check the audio section first with voltage measurements. Double check all part mounting and wire connection to the PC board. Make sure IC1 is inserted properly. You should hear a click or low hum by touching the center terminal of

Fig. 4-15   *The completed IC-FET regenerative receiver ready to be tested.*

the volume control with a screwdriver. Look for poorly soldered connections or broken leads to the outside components. These leads have a tendency to break off after being handled several times. When the circuit is working properly, you can enjoy listening!

Project 3: Two-tube regenerative battery radio

What you will need

L1	25 turns of #24 or #26 enameled magnet wire over 1½-inch form (see text)
L2	108 turns of #24 or #26 enameled magnet wire (see text)
L3	15 turns of #24 or #26 enameled magnet wire (see text)
Q1	1S4 pentode tube
Q2	3S4 pentode miniature battery tube (Antique Electronics Supply)
RFC1	2.5mh choke capacitor (Antique Electronics Supply, PC-1535B or KA7QJY, 2.5 mh)
C1	365-pF variable air capacitor (Antique Electronics Supply, CV-230 or KA7QJY Components, 365 pF)

C2, C4	270-pF, 100-volt silver mica capacitors
C3	0.1-µF, 50-volt ceramic capacitor
C5	0.01-µF, 50-volt ceramic capacitor
R1	2.2-megohm, ½-watt resistor
R2	50-kilohm linear variable control (Mouser Electronics #316-1000
R3	100-kilohm audio taper control
R4	470-kilohm, ½-watt resistor
T1	Driver transformer 10kΩ primary, 2kΩ secondary center-tapped (DC Electronics, 42KL00A or Mouser Electronics, 427L002)
T2	Audio output transformer (Antique Electronics Supply, PT-985 or Mouser Electronics, 42KM003)
B1	Two D cells in series (1.5 V)
B2	Three 9-V batteries in series
Holder (B1)	Flashlight cell holder (Radio Shack, 270-386 or DC Electronics, 12BH121)
Holder (B2)	9-V battery holder (Radio Shack, 270-326 or DC Electronics, H1290)
Tube sockets	Two 7-pin wafer-type tube sockets
J1, J2	Antenna and ground jacks
J3	Stereo headphone jack, molded or open type to fit headphones.
Speaker	4-inch PM speaker.
Misc.	Cabinet parts, bolts and nuts, spacers, hookup wire, solder, etc.
SW1	Double-pole, single-throw toggle switch (DPST)

In a successful marriage, two people can eat cheaper than one, and this also applies to the two-tube regenerative battery radio. Q1 acts as a regenerative detector (1S4), and Q2 acts (3S4) as a power output amplifier. These two tubes are the inexpensive battery-operated types. You can listen to a 3- or 4-inch PM speaker or headphones. A short-circuit headphone jack is included for this purpose.

How the circuit works

The regenerative circuit consists of three coil windings: L1, L2, and L3. (Fig. 4-16). L1 provides better tuning for local stations. L2 and capacitor C1 tune in broadcast stations. Regenerative feedback results with tickler coil L3. RF choke capacitors (RFC1 and C4) provide filtering of the RF signal from the detected audio signal.

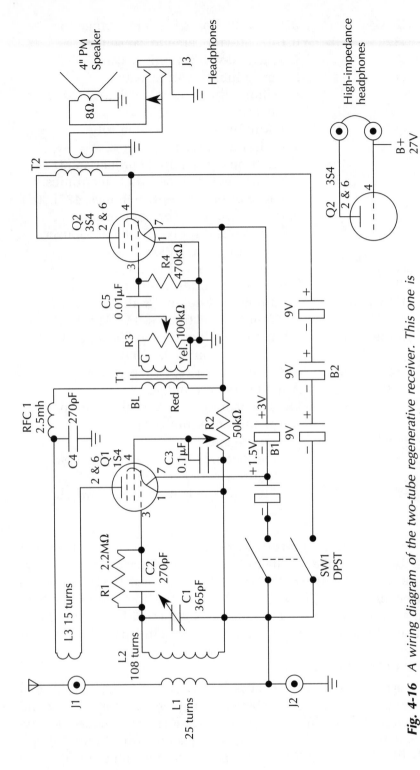

Fig. 4-16 *A wiring diagram of the two-tube regenerative receiver. This one is like those that Grandpa constructed back in the 1920's.*

Transformer coupling is used between Q1 and Q2 for better regeneration control. Resistance and capacitive coupling require less audio signal. Just about any driver transformer can be used that has a 1-kilohm to 10-kilohm impedance primary and a 2-kilohm to 600-kilohm impedance secondary winding. These coupling transformers can be the ultra-miniature or regular mounting types.

The audio signal is controlled with R4 and capacitance-coupled to pin 3 of Q2 (3S4). If a pair of high-impedance headphones are used instead of J1 and a speaker, simply connect them directly to the circuit. Here, a small output transformer (T2) is connected so a permanent magnet (PM) speaker can be used. For low-impedance headphone reception, short jack J3 is installed. For quiet, long distance reception, use headphones.

Both the tube filaments and plate supply are powered with batteries. Two D cells (B1) are connected in series for the filament voltage of Q2, A tap is made for the Q1 filament voltage after the first battery (1.5 V). Three 9-volt batteries (B2) are wired in series for both plate supply voltages. The B2 batteries last longer than the filament batteries (B1) (Fig. 4-17).

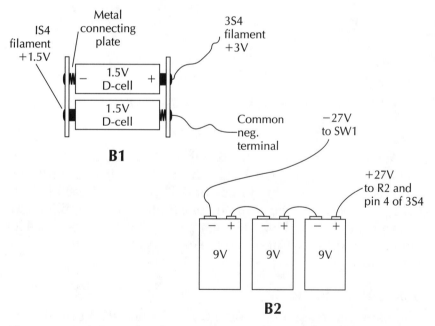

Fig. 4-17 *Both B1 and B2 batteries are wired in series to obtain the correct operating voltage. Both negative battery terminals are soldered to one side of SW1.*

Winding the coils

To make this regenerative radio look antique, the coils were wound on a cardboard or PVC 1½-inch form. First wind 108 turns of #24 or 26 enameled wire for L2 on the center of the coil form. (Fig. 4-18). Holes in the PVC pipe can be poked in the cardboard with an ice pick or a drill can be used. Wind L1 directly over the middle of coil L2. Separate the windings with a layer of masking or transparent tape. Hold the ends with tape until all 25 turns are wound.

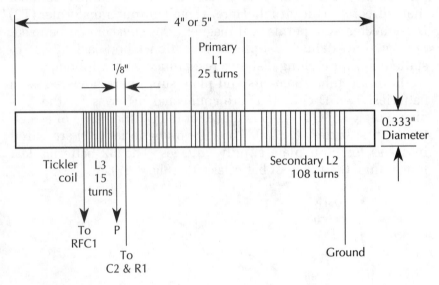

Fig. 4-18 *All three coils are wound with #24 or #26 enameled magnet wire.*

About ⅛ inch away from L2, wind on 15 turns of #24 or 26 enameled wire for L3. Drill holes in the PVC pipe or cardboard form to hold the winding in position. Tape may be used to hold it in position until coil dope or plastic cement is applied. All coils are close wound with about 4 inches of extra wire to use for circuit connections. Cut off all the excess coil wire after the coil is mounted.

Building the chassis

The parts can be mounted on a 3½-×-2⅞-inch PCB or universal board. Lay out both tube sockets on the board. You may use either a PC-type tube socket or a wafer-type socket to mount the tubes on the board. The PC socket mounts on top of the board with the socket pins through the board, or a ⅝-inch hole can be drilled through the board to mount the wafer sockets on the bottom of the board (Fig. 4-19).

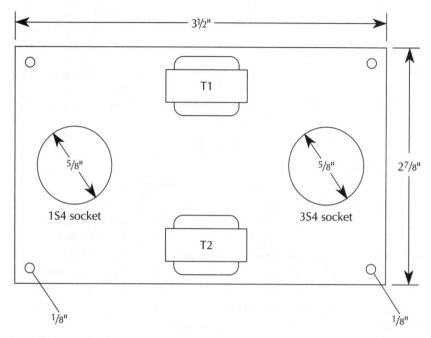

Fig. 4-19 *Tube socket holes can be drilled into the board or mounted on top of the board.*

The rear chassis consists of a 5-×-8-inch piece of wood. Sand the wood until it is clean and free of knicks. Drill four holes to hold the board and parts. Place the board in the center of the rear chassis. The antenna rod, C1, R2, and R3 are mounted on the front panel (Fig. 4-20). The batteries are mounted on the board chassis.

Testing the circuit

Before attempting to operate the radio, double check all wiring. Make sure B1 and B2 are connected properly. Improper connections can damage the filaments in the tubes. Both B1 and B2 are wired in series, with the negative terminal of B1 and B2 soldered to SW1.

Rotate R3 fully to turn on SW1, and turn the volume control all the way up. Set the variable capacitor to its middle frequency, and rotate the regeneration control (R2) until a squeal is

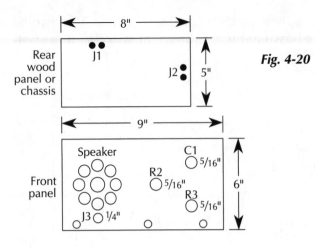

Fig. 4-20 *Rear wood chassis dimensions with holes for J1, J2, and the multipurpose board. C1, R2, R3, the speaker, and the antenna rod are mounted on the front panel.*

heard in the speaker or headphones. Remember that every whistle is a broadcast station.

If you hear no squeal, reverse the L3 windings and try it again. Now tune in a local station. Reduce the regeneration control (R2) until normal audio is heard. Readjustment of R2 and C1 may be needed on weak or distant radio stations. Add 5 more turns on L3 for critical areas. For quiet operation, plug in the low-impedance headphones. A pair of high-impedance headphones can be used by connecting them directly to the plate and B+ line.

Todays radios use ICs and transistors, which are quite efficient when compared to the early regenerative radios. This project, however, teaches you how tubes perform in a regenerative circuit. Why not place this regenerative receiver in a hinged-top lid cabinet with large antique dials and knobs to reflect the original days of regenerative radio construction.

Project 4: The integrated regenerative radio

What you will need

Q1	1S4 pentode tube
IC1	LM386 power IC
RFC1	2.5-mh (KA7QJ7 Components or Mouser Electronics, 434-1250)
C1	95–420-pF trimmer capacitor (Radio Shack, 272-1336 or Antique Electronics Supply, C1-421)
C2	365-pF variable air capacitor (Antique

	Electronics Supply CV-230 or KA7Q5Y Components, 365 pF)
C3, C4	270-pF silver mica capacitor
C5	0.1-μF, 50-volt ceramic capacitor
C6, C7	220-μF, 35-volt electrolytic capacitor
C8	10-μF, 50-volt electrolytic capacitor
C9	10-μF, 50-volt electrolytic capacitor
C11	100-μF, 50-volt ceramic capacitor
L1	21 turns of #24 or #26 enameled wire
L2	108 turns of #24 or #26 enameled wire
L3	15 turns, #24 or #26 enameled wire
R1	2.2-megohm ½-watt resistor
R2	50-kilohm linear taper control (Mouser Electronics #316-1000
R3	10-kilohm audio taper control
R4	10-ohm, ½-watt resistor
SW2	Double-pole, single-throw (DPST) toggle switch
T1	Driver transformer 10kΩ primary, 2kΩ secondary center-tapped (DC Electronics, 42KL002 or Mouser Electronics, 427 U002)
PCB	Dual mini-board
J1	Stereo mini earphone jack. (Radio Shack, 276-148)
B1	Two D cell flashlight batteries
B2	Three 9-volt batteries
Holders (B1)	Two-cell socket (Radio Shack, 270-3869 or DC Electronics, 12BH121)
Holders (B2)	Three battery holders (Radio Shack, 270-326A or DC Electronics, 1290)
Tube socket	Wafer type (Antique Electronics Supply PS-201)
Misc.	9-volt snap sockets & leads, wire, solder, bolts & nuts, etc.

The integrated AM radio combines the early tube regenerative circuit and the present day IC audio output circuit. An 1S4 tube acts as regenerative detector, and the LM386 IC is used for low-impedance headphone reception. In fact, the whole receiver can be constructed for about the cost of a pair of high-impedance headphones (Fig. 4-21). On strong local stations, the audio stage can drive a 4-inch PM speaker, if desired.

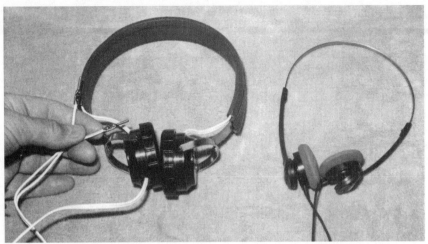

Fig. 4-21   *High-impedance (2000 ohm) and low-impedance (42 ohm) headphones.*

How the circuit works

The RF signal is picked up at the red antenna post and coupled to the tuned circuit via variable capacitor C1 (Fig. 4-22). C1 should be adjusted so that all weak signals are heard across the entire broadcast band. Sometimes adjustment of C1 can help eliminate annoying strong local stations. L1 and C2 tune in the broadcast band. SW1 switches the primary stage in or out for re-curring weak stations.

R1 and C3 provide tube 1S4 grid-leak detection. A feedback signal from coil L2 provides high gain and regeneration sensitiv-ity. If the set does not oscillate (no squeal is heard), simply re-verse the connections of L2. C4 and RF choke coil RFC1 provide filtering of the audio signal.

Q1 has a 1.5-volt filament voltage provided by two D cells in parallel. The filament current is only 105 millamperes. The plate voltage is furnished with +27 volts from three 9-volt batteries wired in series. Because Q1 pulls less than 6 milliamperes of cur-rent, B2 batteries will last much longer than the D cells. Notice that the first 9-volt battery is tapped to power IC1. Regeneration is controlled with R2 (50 kilohms).

The audio signal is coupled through C8 and fed to the volume control (R3). The controlled audio is then fed to pin 3 of IC1. Here the audio signal is boosted by IC1 and coupled to stereo headphone jack J3 through C9. The supply voltage at pin 6 of IC1 is 9 volts from the first 9-volt B2 battery. Although the integrated receiver may

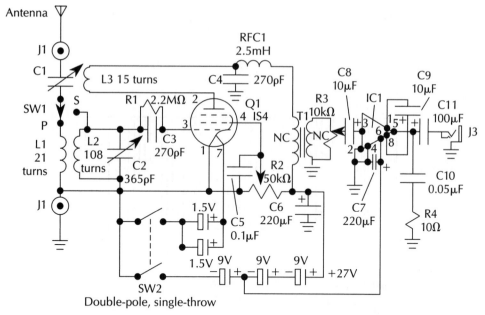

Fig. 4-22 *An integrated AM radio with a 1S4 pentode tube and IC1.*

drive a speaker, headphone reception works best. An inexpensive pair of low-impedance headphones can be used in this receiver.

Winding the coils

Wind 108 turns of #24 or #26 enameled wire over a 1½-inch form (L2). Holes may be drilled through the PVC pipe, or tape can be applied to prevent the wire from unraveling until all the coils are wound. Start winding L3 ⅛ inch from the end of L2. Wind on 15 turns of wire. Fasten the coil with tape. Now wind on 21 turns for coil L1 over the center of L2. Place a layer of tape over L2 before winding L1 (Fig. 4-23).

Place coil dope at the ends of each coil so the wires do not unwind. Remove the tape holding the coil ends after the coil dope has set. You can also use clear fingernail polish, model plastic cement, or rubber silicone cement to hold the coil wires in position.

Mount the coil behind the variable capacitor (C2) with the L3 winding close to pin 2 of the Q1 socket. C1 can be mounted on terminal SW1. Try to keep all RF wires as short as possible.

Building the chassis

Q1 and IC1 are mounted on a dual IC mini-board. Q1 is mounted on one of the boards and IC1 is mounted on the other. Keep the

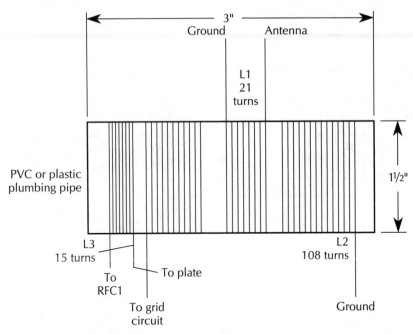

Fig. 4-23 *The primary winding of L1 has 21 turns of #24 or #26 enameled wire; L2 has 108 turns; and L3 has 15 turns of wire. All are wound on 1½-inch PVC pipe form.*

regenerative detector parts away from the audio output circuits, The 7-pin socket can be a PC-type socket or a wafer-type socket mounted above the board with the center shield hole drilled through the PCB. Bare wires can be connected between the pins and the underside terminals to complete the circuit (Fig. 4-24).

Mount IC1 at the center of the other dual IC mini-board with the audio output leads away from the regenerative detector. The only components requiring connections between the two circuits are C6 and R4. The mini-board can be lifted off the plastic cabinet with metal or plastic ½-inch spacers.

Mounting parts

Start your wiring with the RF circuit and tube socket. Keep R1 and C3 close to the Q1 socket. Bring C2, L2 and L3 leads out of the end of the board for easy connections. The coil form should be mounted with short extension leads close to Q1. Mount C4 and RFC1 close to L3. Connect extension wires for regeneration control R2.

Mount the IC1 socket in the center of the second mini-board. Bend over each IC pin. All the small parts in the audio section

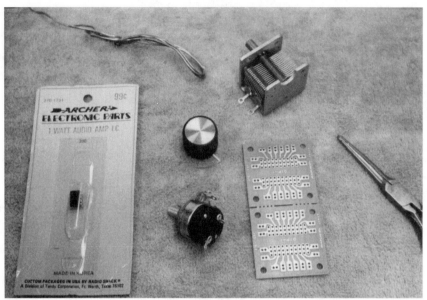

Fig. 4-24   *The tube socket, transformer, IC, and all small parts are mounted on a dual IC mini-board.*

are mounted as they are wired into the circuit. Keep C8 close to terminal pin 6 of IC1. Extend the headphone wires from C11 at the opposite end of the board. Connect extension wires for the volume control (R4).

When wiring up the batteries, make sure the negative terminal of B1 and B2 are connected to SW2. Connect both D cells in parallel by soldering the end terminals together (Fig. 4-25). All three 9-volt batteries are wired in series. After the first 9-volt battery, run a tap wire to pin 6 of IC1. IC1 operates from one 9-volt battery while 27 volts is needed for Q1 and the regeneration action.

Testing the circuit

Connect a pair of low-impedance headphones into J1. Connect antenna and ground to their respective posts. Rotate R2. You should hear feedback when the control is almost fully turned. Rotate C2 until you hear several loud whistle or squealing noises. Remember, each whistle or squeal is a broadcast station. If C1 is adjusted too tightly, regeneration may cease.

Adjust R2 slowly until you can hear the audio signal. This signal is weaker on distant stations. First try it on your own local stations. Learn how to adjust the regeneration and volume control for sufficient sound. Change SW1 to the primary wind-

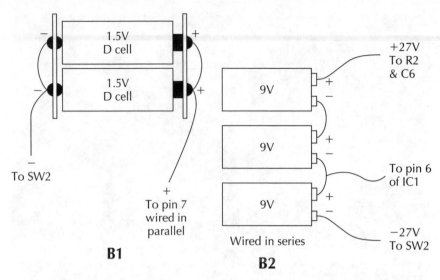

B1   **B2**

Fig. 4-25 *Connect the D cells in parallel and the three 9-volt batteries in series.*

ing to help eliminate strong local stations. C1 may be adjusted for weaker stations. The optimum setting of C1 is when stations can be heard over the whole broadcast band without interference.

Troubleshooting the circuit

If no stations are heard, make sure the audio output stage is functioning. Try touching a screwdriver blade to the volume control (R4). If a click and hum is heard in the headphones, the audio is normal, so go to the front-end stages. Inject a 1 kHz audio signal at the center pin (7) of R4 to test the audio output stages.

Double check the wiring of IC1 if no sound can be heard. Compare the voltage measurements on IC1 terminals with those shown on the schematic. Be careful not to short any pins together. Insert a current meter between the 9-volt battery and pin 6 of IC1. If IC1 reads over 20 mA of current, suspect a leaky IC or improper wiring. Make sure pin 1 of IC1 is correctly inserted in the IC socket.

When the audio stages are normal but you have no reception, reverse the leads of L3. Now adjust the regeneration control with the volume control fully turned. Touch the antenna terminal with your finger (with the antenna removed) and you should hear a scratchy noise. You should hear whistling and howling noises as C2 is rotated. If you do not, check all voltages on Q1. Be careful not to short the filament terminals with a B+ voltage (Fig. 4-26). If the circuit is working normally, you should hear a loud

Fig. 4-26 *When troubleshooting the circuit, the ground terminal is used for the common (black) probe, while the red probe measures voltages on the tube and the IC.*

clicking noise when touching pin 2 or 3. Place the ground terminal (black) on ground post when taking voltage measurements.

You may switch to a 4-inch PM speaker on strong broadcast stations. Readjust C1, SW1 and C2 as necessary for weaker stations. In the evening hours, the receiver picks up quite a few stations. In fact, AM stations were heard over 1000 miles away —Happy Listening!!

Shortwave radio projects

THE SHORTWAVE (SW) FREQUENCY BANDS ARE FULL OF excitement. A good outside antenna is needed for shortwave reception, since these signals are weaker than AM radio. Ham radio operators can use shortwave bands, beginning with frequencies of 160 meters (1,800–2,000 kHz) to 10 meters (28,000–29,700 kHz). International broadcasting stations also use shortwave bands, and operate at 49 meters (5,800–6,200 kHz) to 11 meters (25,600–26,100 kHz) (Table 5-1).

Table 5-1
The Ham and International Radio
band of frequencies. Besides AM, the
amateur radio operator uses single-sideband
(SSB) and continuous wave (CW) frequencies.

	kHz		kHz
160 meters	1800–2000	CW	7000–7150
80 meters	3500–4000	SSB	7150–7300
40 meters	7000–7300	CW	14000–14200
20 meters	14000–14350	SSB	14000–14350
15 meters	21000–21450	CW	21000–21250
10 meters	28000–29000	SSB	21250–21450
CW	3500–3800	CW	28000–28500
SSB	3800–4000	SSB	28500–29700

Broadcast stations in tropical regions have special bands set aside, since shortwave (SW) is the only way to reach these areas (Table 5-2). The remaining SW bands are filled with aeronautical and military stations. Of course, these stations usually use single sideband (SSB) or continuous wave (CW) and are found outside the amateur and broadcast bands (Table 5-3). Ships and coastal stations can also be heard on shortwave frequencies. Most communications are either SSB or CW. The international distress signal is 2,9182 kHz (Table 5-4).

Meters	kHz
120	2300–2500
90	3200–3400
75	3900–4000
60	4750–5060

Table 5-2
Tropical broadcast station frequencies on shortwave (SW).

kHz
4650–4750
6545–6765
8815–9040
10000–10100
11175–11400
13200–13360
15010–15100
17900–18030

Table 5-3
Aircraft sideband and AM frequencies on the shortwave band.

kHz
4063–4139
4361–4438
8195–8181
12330–12420
13107–13200
16460–16565

Table 5-4
Ship and coastal station frequencies in the shortwave band.

If you have not listened to shortwave stations before, you might become confused by the many frequencies and variety of signals found there. It can be confusing when an international broadcast station states the station call sign and the operating frequency of 7.5 MHz; this is the same as 41 meters or 7,500 kHz. Tuning in regenerative receivers can also be confusing at first. Critical regeneration control adjustments can be perfected with a few minutes' practice. The regenerative receiver pulls in more SW stations than any other radio, and it only uses a few parts. It is best to try the shortwave receiver out at night or early in the morning when there is best reception.

So, let's build a few SW receivers, starting with a simple crystal shortwave receiver, then several regenerative radios, and finally ending up with a superhet SW special receiver.

Project 1: Crystal shortwave radio

What you will need

D1	IN34 fixed crystal-diode
IC1	LM386 low-power IC
C1	365-pF air variable capacitor
C2	0.1-µF, 50-volt ceramic capacitor
C3, C5	220-µF, 15-volt electrolytic capacitor
C4	10-µF, 15-volt electrolytic capacitor
C6	0.047-µF, 50-volt ceramic capacitor
L1, L2	2½ turns for L1, and 24 turns for L2 of #24 enameled wire on a T-50-2 toroid core form
T-50-2	Toroid ½-inch ferrite iron core
R1	10-kilohm audio with SW1
R2	10-Ω, ½-watt resistor
J1, J2	Red and black antenna posts
J3	Stereo miniature low-impedance headphone jack
SW1	Single-pole, single-throw (SPST) switch on rear of R1
B1	9-volt battery
Misc.	Piece of PCB, bolts, rubber feet, 8-pin IC socket, solder, low-impedance 8- to 48-ohm headphones, etc.

Although the little crystal shortwave receiver has no RF amplification, you would be surprised how well it works. After completing this SW radio, it was connected to a 60-foot length of antenna about 30 feet high, and four international shortwave stations were heard (Fig. 5-1)!

How the circuit works

This experimental shortwave receiver has a homemade toroid coil and variable capacitor C1 to tune in SW stations between 5 and 22.5 MHz. No RF or IF amplification is found in this circuit. Diode D1 rectifies the RF signal to audio. Instead of placing high-impedance headphones at this point, the IC amp (IC1) was inserted (Fig. 5-2). In fact, the IC amp and inexpensive headphones cost less than a pair of high-impedance headphones. Besides that you have a lot more audio, and the low-impedance headphones can be purchased most anywhere for under $5. A good pair of high-impedance headphones are difficult to obtain.

R1 controls the audio and is left fully open. C2 couples the audio signal to pin 3 of IC1. This low-powered IC (LM386) works

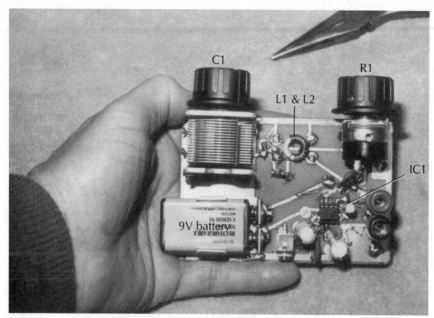

Fig. 5-1   *All parts are mounted on top of the PCB.*

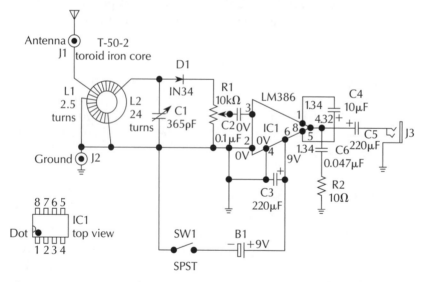

Fig. 5-2   *Notice there are no RF or IF amplifier components found in this SW radio.*

well in the headphone circuit. Capacitor C5 couples the amplified audio to J3 for low-impedance headphone reception. IC1 is powered with a 9-volt battery. Switch SW1 is mounted on the rear of R1, acting as an ON/OFF switch.

Winding the coils

The toroid core has a ½-inch outside diameter and can take up to 37 turns of #24 enameled wire. This coil requires only 24 turns. Cut off a piece of wire 17 inches long and start by leaving one inch of wire for connecting the coil to the circuit. Wind the wire as tight and close together as possible until you have wound 24 turns on the core (Fig. 5-3).

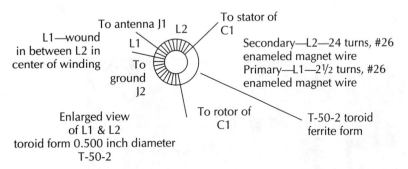

Fig. 5-3   *Wind 24 turns of #26 enameled magnet wire on a T50-2 toroid form for L2 and 2½ turns for L1.*

When pushing excess wire through the hole, be careful not to put a kink in the coil wire. Pull each turn tight. The wire will hold its shape.

Wind 2½ turns on the primary (L1), and place it between the turns of L2 in the middle of the L2 winding. Work the wire between the L2 windings. Tin each wire end with a 150-watt or larger soldering iron. Extreme heat helps make a good solder connection. The enamel coating will melt off.

Place the L1 connections toward the antenna and the ground PC wiring. Cut approximately ¼-inch leads on the wire. Solder each end of coil directly on the board. After the variable capacitor (C1) is mounted, solder the stator terminal to the secondary winding and to D1. Although mounting bolts hold the capacitor in place, solder a bare ground wire between the rotor (outside of the capacitor) and the copper ground.

Laying out the PC board

The PC board (PCB) and chassis were cut from a larger piece of one-sided board. This PCB wires the components together and serves as the main chassis. No holes are drilled into the board except the antenna and ground connections, the variable capacitor bolts, and holes for the headphone jack. The rest of the parts are mounted on top of the board. Four corner feet are fastened to the bottom side.

Lay out the PC wiring as shown in Fig. 5-4. Keep the antenna and ground connections apart. C1 and the 9-volt battery holder mount in the large block or ground section. Be sure to place the IC socket so that there is room to plug in IC1 without disturbing the other parts.

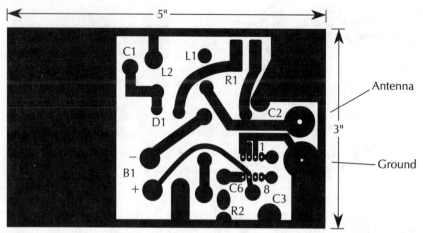

Fig. 5-4   *Layout of the PCB wiring. This PCB was cut from a larger copper-clad board.*

R1 terminals are soldered directly on the larger areas of the PCB wiring, with the ground side to the ground section of the board. Bend the terminals at a slant, and solder them for correct wiring. Then straighten R1 and solder a ground wire to switch SW1 so R1 is level with the board. Make sure the board is square before the variable control is soldered into position.

After all PC transfers are placed on the copper board, you can put the board in the etching fluid. Before you do, place a wooden pencil under the center of the etching container, so you can rock it when the board is placed inside. This helps provide quicker etching time. The board should be etched in thirty minutes. Double check all wiring junctions after etching. Sometimes etching the board too long can destroy wire connections. Bridge any gaps with bare hookup wire.

Drill two $\frac{5}{32}$-inch holes to mount the antenna and ground posts. Next mark the bottom mounting holes of C1. It's best to use a piece of paper on the bottom and the front edge of the capacitor as a guide. Push the capacitor mounting holes through the paper with the point of a pencil. Now lay the piece of paper down on the spot where C1 is to be mounted, and mark the holes.

Mounting parts

Be careful when mounting the variable capacitor because if you use bolts that are too long, you can throw the stator plates out of line. Cut off the mounting bolts so they are just long enough to go through the PCB with ¹⁄₁₆-inch extra. These are very short bolts, but they can be made using a vise with a hacksaw, and then ground on a grinder with a file. Always place a nut into the bolt before cutting or grinding it to length so that the threads are not ruined.

Next mount the IC socket since the prongs must be bent outward and flattened. Make sure each prong is soldered to the correct PC wiring. Do not let solder run over into the next connection. Inspect your soldering job with a hand magnifying glass, or perform a continuity test from each terminal (on the top side) to the first wired component.

Mount all small parts next. Solder each part as it is mounted. Be careful not to let excess solder touch other connections. Remember, these parts are mounted directly on top of the bare PC wiring. Cut component leads short and bend them over the PC wiring connection. Coil L1 and L2 can be cemented to the board after the receiver is tested (Fig. 5-5).

Fig. 5-5 *How all the parts are mounted on the PCB surface.*

Mount C1 and R1 last. R1 is rigid when all three lugs are soldered to the board. Make sure R1 is level before soldering the back switch wires. The ground and antenna post lugs are soldered to their respective copper wiring. Double check that all component leads do not touch any other leads.

Testing the circuit

Attach a 9-volt battery to the circuit. To do this, slip it in from behind and push it into position. Make sure the switch is OFF. Correctly insert IC1 in the 8-pin socket. Keep the white dot (number one marking) towards the front end of IC1. Inspect the IC closely to be sure all pins are in the correct socket holes. Sometimes one or two can slide off to one side. Plug in a pair of inexpensive, low-impedance headphones.

Now rotate R1 fully. Touch the cathode of D1 with a small metal screwdriver. You should hear a hum. When the contact is touched with the screwdriver, a scratching noise can be heard in the headphones if the amp is working. Hook up the antenna and the ground wires.

If no hum or scratching noise is heard, check the voltages on each IC pin. Compare them with the schematic. Check the current across SW1 with R1 turned OFF. You should measure under 10 mA. Make sure all connections are soldered correctly. Double check the PCB for improperly dripped solder connections. Make certain all the board wiring is correct by following from each IC pin to the corresponding component.

Apply four rubber feet on the bottom of the chassis once the radio is working to prevent the unit from sliding around. Try tuning in SW stations late at night or early in the morning. Tune slowly with a large knob. When you locate a weak station, wait a few seconds and it will come in loud and clear.

Project 2: 31-to 75-meter regenerative tube radio

What you will need

Q1	1S4 miniature battery tube
C1	6–50-pF trimmer capacitor (Radio Shack 272-1340 or Antique Electronics Supply, CV-421)
C2	140 pF (KA7QJY components, 140 pF—90 pF Dual Air Cap or Antique Electronics Supply, CV471)

C3	27-pF silver mica capacitor
C4	0.1-µF, 50-V ceramic capacitor
C5	270-pF silver mica capacitor
C6	0.001-µF, 50-V ceramic capacitor
L1	7 turns of #24 enameled wire
L2	13 turns of #24 enameled wire
L3	6 turns of #24 enameled wire
L4	9 turns of #24 enameled wire
L5	6 turns of #24 enameled wire
R1	2.2-megohm, ½-watt resistor
R2	50-kilohm linear taper control with (Mouser Electronics, #316-1000
SW2	Double-pole, single-throw (DPST) toggle switch
RFC1	2.5-mh (KA7QJY Components)
J1, J2	Speaker output posts (Radio Shack, 274-315)
B1	Two C cells(1.5 V) connected in parallel
B2	Three 9-V batteries connected in series
Tube socket	7-pin wafer (Antique Electronics Supply, PS-201)
B1	Battery holder (Radio Shack, 270-385 or DC Electronics, 2227)
B2	Clip 9-V leads, three total
Headphones	High-impedance (2000 ohm), or use the IC amp and low-impedance phones.
SW1	Alligator clip
Misc.	Wood chassis, metal front panel, hookup wire, solder, wood screws, etc.

During the early 1930's, regenerative tube radios were very popular. Most shortwave receivers operated from batteries. Number 30, 32, 33 and 34 tubes were used in many early shortwave receivers. Today, these tubes are too expensive and too difficult to obtain. Most of these antique regenerative radios were built on a breadboard with phenolic front panels.

You can put yourself back in the 1930's by building this regenerative tube shortwave radio (Fig. 5-6). This receiver tunes in the 31-meter to 75-meter band (9.6–4 MHz). A 1.5-volt battery tube (1S4) was chosen for its availability and because it can be purchased for about $3. Although the volume is fairly weak because shortwave signals are weaker than the broadcast band, you can still get the idea of how the regenerative shortwave receiver performs. You can also connect the small IC amp and operate it

Fig. 5-6   *The regenerative receiver tuned to an international broadcast station.*

with low-impedance headphones and you will have volume to spare.

How the circuit works

The regenerative shortwave circuit is similar to the broadcast radio, except less wire is used in the coils and a smaller tuning capacitor is needed. Feedback is accomplished with a plate tickler coil, and regeneration is controlled with a 50-kΩ variable resistor.

A 140-pF tuning capacitor is used instead of a larger 365-pF type (Fig. 5-7). These tuning capacitors are still available from several sources. You may be able to pick one up at a surplus store or you can trim one down to the correct size. To do this, just remove stator plates until 4 or 5 plates are left. The tuning capacitor in Fig. 5-8 was taken from an old radio, and the plates were removed as needed.

The tuning capacitor used in this regenerative radio is a new dual-miniature type (100 pF and 140 pF), with only the 140-pF section being used. These tuning capacitors are available in a range from 135 pF to 140 pF. All you need is one 140-pF section for this small tube radio.

The shortwave signal is picked up by the antenna and coupled to L1 through trimmer capacitor C1. Adjustment of C1 is made to cover both shortwave bands. Although SW1 is nothing more than a small alligator clip, it could be replaced with a double-pole, single-throw (DPST) toggle switch. Resistor R1 and capacitor C3 provide grid leak detection. The tickler winding is taken from the plate terminal (pins 2&6 of Q1), and fed back to the grid coil.

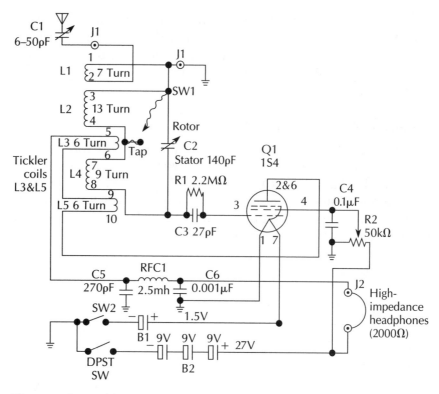

Fig. 5-7 *A variable tuning capacitor with stator blades removed for 140-pF capacitance.*

Fig. 5-8 *One-tube regenerative radio operating in the 40- and 80-meter range.*

The RF signal is bypassed and filtered to ground after detection, by C5, C6, and a 2.5-mh RF choke (RFC) coil. Regeneration is controlled by feeding a variable voltage to pin 4 of Q1. A high-impedance pair of headphones (2000 Ω) are placed between the plate circuit of Q1 and the B+ voltage (27 V).

Connecting the batteries

The filament of the 1S4 tube (Q1) is powered with a 1.5-volt source. To provide longer battery life, two C cells were connected in parallel (Fig. 5-9). Terminals 1 and 7 of Q1 are the tube filament connections. The B+ source consists of three 9-volt batteries wired in series. These three batteries stand on one end so they do not take up too much room.

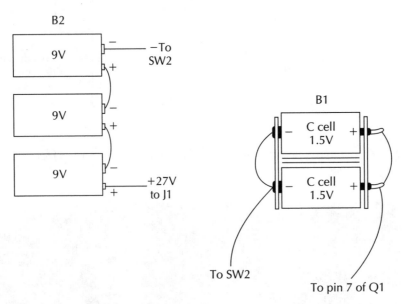

Fig. 5-9 *Connect the C cells in parallel and the 9-volt batteries in series. The filament voltage for the tube is 1.5 volts, and the plate voltage is +27 V.*

You will find that when regeneration control R2 is almost halfway rotated, feedback occurs. This means that the 27 volts (B+ source) provides audio volume and regeneration action. If the set won't oscillate, reverse the plate coil connections. If the coil is wound and connected as shown, no regeneration problems should occur.

Winding the coils

The regenerative tube radio is designed to pull in the 31–75-meter bands. WWV can be heard in the middle of the tuning capacitor range (5000 kHz) with L4 in the circuit. When switch SW1 (the alligator clip) is hooked on top of L4, the circuit is tuned to the 40-meter band. Amateur, international, broadcast, and CW can be heard in each band of frequencies.

All 5 coil windings are wound on a plastic 35-mm film container. L2 and L4 provide reception for the 80-meter band, while L4 is tapped for the 40-meter band reception (Fig. 5-10).

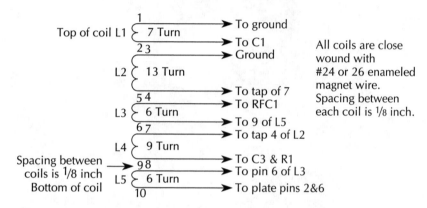

Fig. 5-10 *How to wind L1, L2, and L3 with taps. This receiver tunes in the 40- and 80-meter range of frequencies.*

Start with L5 at the cap end of the plastic container. Keep the plastic cap on to provide support until all the coils are wound and glued into position. Leave about 3 inches for each coil connection. They can be tinned and cut off when they are wired into the circuit. The end wire (#10 on the schematic) goes to the plate terminal (pins 2 or 6) of Q1. Next wind on L4 (9 turns), followed by L3, L2 and L1. Both tickler coils (L3 and L5) consist of 6 turns of #24 enameled wire. The grid coil (L2) has 13 turns, and the primary antenna coil (L1) has 7 turns. Regeneration occurs in both bands with tickler coils L3 and L5 wound in this fashion. All coils are close wound with #24 enameled wire.

Mounting parts

Mount C3 and R2 on the front metal panel. The rest of the large components are mounted on the board chassis. Keep the flashlight batteries to the right side and to the rear of the chassis. The antenna and ground jacks are also mounted near the coil towards the rear of the chassis. The coil is held to the chassis with a wood screw inserted through the plastic lid of the 35-mm container. Mount all RF components as close as possible (Fig. 5-11).

Fig. 5-11   *Top view of the tube radio showing how the various parts are mounted.*

Mount the tube socket in the middle of the board with ½-inch plastic supports. Keep all RF components up off of the wood base, including the antenna and ground terminals. Dual-speaker terminal posts are used for antenna and ground and headphone jacks J1 and J2. Mount these terminal strips up off the chassis with plastic spacers.

Wiring the circuit

Make all wiring connections as direct as possible. Especially use short connections within the RF circuits. Cut and connect all coil leads as short as possible. The terminal strip should be mounted near the tube socket for mounting the RFC choke, C5, and C6.

Connect the battery terminals first. Make sure the negative terminals of the 1.5-volt and 27-volt supplies connect to one side of switch SW2. Terminal 1 of Q1 goes to ground and to one side of the switch. The positive terminal of the 1.5-volt batteries goes to terminal 7. Connect the three 9-volt batteries in series with the positive terminal on the headphone post (J2).

Connect coil L3 terminals so that plate terminal 2 (pin 2 of Q1) is next to grid coil L2. The other end is connected to RFC1 at the terminal strip. The bottom winding of L1 and L2 are tied to ground. Solder a lead with a small alligator clip to ground. Make this lead just long enough to reach the top of coil L2.

Building the front and rear panel

The radio is mounted on a wood chassis. Fir, ash, or oak board is fine as long as it's clean and dry. In fact, a piece of decorative pine found at hobby and craft stores works great. Just cut it to the size shown in Fig. 5-12. Make all jack and tube socket holes on the board. Drill ¹⁄₁₆-inch holes, so wood screws can be easily started.

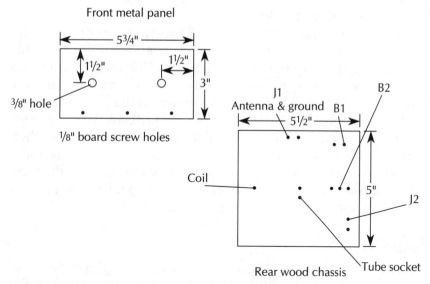

Fig. 5-12 *Rear wood chassis and front panel (metal) dimensions and required holes.*

C1 and R2 are mounted on the front metal panel. Use metal instead of masonite or plastic to prevent stray capacitance from your hand while operating the tuning capacitor and the regeneration control. If C1 does not have front mounting holes, make a metal bracket and bolt it at the bottom of the front metal panel.

Before mounting any parts, place dry transfer letters and dial on the front panel. Lay out each dial indicator and number. Spray with clear lacquer or acrylic spray to protect the front panel finish and the transfers.

Testing the circuit

Connect outside ground and antenna wires to the regenerative receiver. Connect a pair of high-impedance headphones. Rotate R2 halfway. The circuit is oscillating when whistling is heard as the tuning capacitor is turned. If you do not hear whistling, rotate R2 until you hear feedback. Now you should hear squealing and whistling of stations as C2 is rotated. If you do not, reverse the leads of coil L3.

You hear overseas shortwave frequencies anywhere from 7500 kHz (40 meters) to 59,800 kHz (49 meters). Ham AM and SSB bands are heard at 8000 and 7300 kHz, CW is heard at 3800 and 7100 kHz. The WWV (National Bureau of Standards) time broadcast is heard at 5000 kHz.

Although tuning controls C2 and R2 are quite sensitive, careful tuning can pull in many stations. Continuous wave and AM are the easiest stations to tune in. Rotate R2 until CW stations are sharp and clear. Set C1 so that there are no dead spots on the dial. This shortwave receiver picks up stations all across the band range.

Single sideband (SSB) tuning is very critical. If you manage to pick up a group of ham radio operators talking to one another, you will notice that the regeneration control is set quite high. The voices sound garbled. To remedy that, carefully adjust the tuning capacitor until voices are clear. SSB operation can be improved by adding more audio and using finer tuning.

Tuning hints

Fine tuning the variable capacitor (C2) can be improved by moving it more slowly. Use either a large knob or a vernier dial on the shaft. The vernier dial assembly can be added to the front panel instead of a regular knob. Reduction gear shaft assemblies can also be added to slow the rotation of C2. Bandspread tuning can also be added, as you will see in the next shortwave receiver project.

Although the volume from this one-tube receiver is audible, increase the audio by connecting the small IC amp (found in Chapter 2) to the circuit. Do not connect the input directly to the headphone jacks (J2). Instead, clip a driver interstage transformer between the radio and the audio amp. A 600-to 600-ohm, 1.5-k to

600-ohm, 2-k to 600-ohm, or a 10-k to 600-ohm driver transformer will work. You can use a standard, miniature, microminiature, or ultraminiature core transformer in the circuit.

Clip the primary winding to the phone jacks (J2). Clip the small input terminals of the IC amp to the secondary leads. Clip a lead between the common ground of the amp and the receiver together. Now you will have plenty of volume, even on the weakest shortwave station (Fig. 5-13).

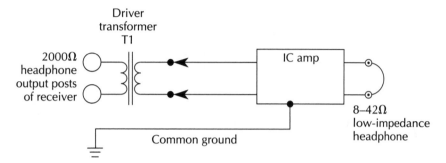

Fig. 5-13 *For more audio, this figure shows how the small IC amp is connected to the high impedance headphone jack (J2).*

You might want to construct the IC amp and regenerative radio on one PC board (Fig. 5-14 on page 148). Use a PC-type tube socket for Q1 and an 8-pin DIP IC socket for IC1. Be sure to keep the RF signals away from the audio output. All small components can be mounted on the PC board. The regeneration, volume, and tuning controls can be mounted on the front metal panel. First build and test the amplifier section before building the regenerative circuit.

Your first shortwave receiver should cause a lot of excitement and fun. So sit back and enjoy!

Project 3: Double-T shortwave radio

L1, L2	Three band plug-in coils on plug-in coil forms (Antique Electronics Supply, PC-987
C1	6–50-pF trimmer capacitor (Radio Shack, 272-13, or Antique Electronics Supply, CV-421)
C2	15-pF variable air capacitor (KA7QJY Components, 15pF or Ocean State Electronics, 167-1)
C3	100-pF variable air capacitor (KA7QJY Com-

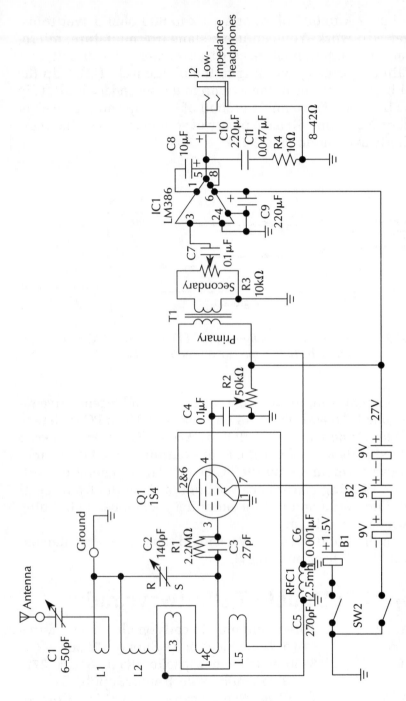

Fig. 5-14 *You may want to build the IC amp and shortwave regenerative radio on one PC board with a metal front panel. Here is the complete schematic.*

	ponents, 100 pF–200 pF–300 pF (use one section) or 90 pF–140 pF (use 90-pF section) or Ocean State Electronics, MC-100 M or HF 100)
C4	50-pF, 100-V silver mica capacitor
C5	0.1-µF, 100-V ceramic capacitor
C6	270-pF silver mica capacitor
C7	0.001-µF, 100-V ceramic capacitor
C8	0.01-µF, 100-V ceramic capacitor
C9	35-µF, 35-V electrolytic capacitor
C10, C11	100-µF, 100-V electrolytic capacitor
C12	1000-µF, 100-V electrolytic capacitor
L1	Three-bond plug-in coils using #24 enameled wire. 8 turns (20 meter), 15 turns (40 meter), 32 turns (80 meter)
L2	7 turns (20 meter), 8 turns (40 meter), 13 turns (80 meter)
R1	2.2-megohm, ½-watt resistor
R2	5-kilohm linear variable control
R3	50-kilohm linear variable control
R4	100-kilohm audio taper control
R5	470-kilohm, ½-watt resistor
R6	270-ohm, ½-watt resistor
R7	470-ohm, 1-watt resistor
T1	Interstage linear transformer (Ocean State Electronics, 45-707 10k to 70 ohms or Antique Electronics Supply PT-125A or D.C. Electronics 42XL002, 10KCT-2KCT)
T2	Ac, 25.2-volt step-down transformer
Tube	12AT7 tube (Antique Electronics Supply)
J1, J2, J3	Speaker jack strip (Radio Shack, 274-315)
RFC1	2.5-mh choke coil (KA7QJY Components, 2.5 mh)
Venier dial	0–100 (Ocean Electronics, VD112-100 or Mouser Electronics, 45KN100)
Front panel	Phenolic panel (Antique Electronics Supply, SM-710)
SW1	Single-pole, single-throw (SPST) switch on rear of volume control R4
Rear panel	5-×7-inch piece of ash or firwood
Misc.	Piece of double-sided PCB, ½ of a dual-IC board, solder, bolts, nuts, screws, ac cord coil socket, tube socket

In 1934, one-tube shortwave sets were quite famous (Fig. 5-15). These receivers pick up stations on the ham bands, 80, 40, and 20 meters. The unique thing about this receiver is that it uses plug-in coils. You can find these plug-in coils at various part suppliers. So, let's get started!

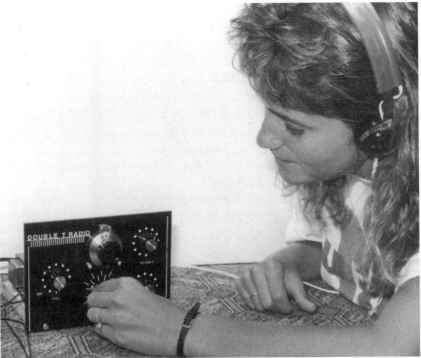

Fig. 5-15 *The Double-T shortwave receiver with 80-, 40-, and 20-meter plug-in coils.*

How the circuit works

The regenerative circuit of the T shortwave radio consists of a doubletriode tube (12 AT7) acting as a detector and an audio amplifier, which explains the name double-T (dual triode). Three different plug-in coils are used to cover the 80-, 40-and 20-meter bands. Grid coil L1 and C3 tunes in the desired station (Fig. 5-16). Variable capacitor C2 provides bandspread and is rotated with a vernier dial to select stations. C4 and R1 provide grid leak detection.

Tickler coil L2 feeds back the signal from the plate element of Q1 (pin 1) to the grid coil circuits. It must be wound in the same direction as shown, with the connections shown, to provide feedback oscillations. If it does not, simply reverse connections

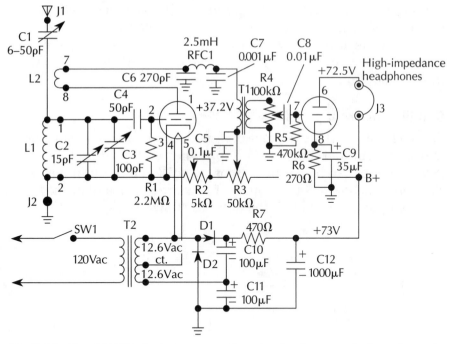

Fig. 5-16   *The 12AT7 tube in a regenerative circuit using one triode as the regenerative detector and the other as the amplifier.*

to leads 7 and 8. The RF choke coil (RFC1), C6, and C7 provide an RF filter network, separating the audio signal to T1.

Voltage is supplied from R3 to the primary winding of interstage tuner transformer T1, and on to the plate of Q1. R3 and R2 control regeneration. R2 is tuned fully open and R3 is adjusted just to the point of oscillation. Then R2 is reduced to fine tune that point of oscillation. Select a driver transformer with the highest resistance windings.

The audio signal is coupled to the volume control (R4), by the secondary winding of T1. C8 couples the audio and blocks dc voltage at grid terminal 7 of Q1. R6 and C9 provide cathode bias for the audio portion of the tube. Pin 6 is connected to the headphone jack (J3).

Building the power supply

Dc voltage (B+) is applied to R3 and J3 from an ac power supply. The step-down transformer (T2) primary winding feeds into a full-wave voltage-doubler circuit. Since tubes require higher voltages than solid-state devices, the voltage-doubler circuit increases the voltage. D1 and D2 provide full-wave rectification of the ac voltage, and it is fed to filter components R7 and C12. The heater voltage at pins 4 and 5 are taken from center tap and one side of the secondary winding of T2. No power line hum is heard in the headphones.

Building the front panel

For the front panel, use a piece of ⅜₆-inch black phenolic panel or masonite. Antique Electronics Supply has an 8-×-12-inch piece (SM-710) that can be cut in two for two different radio projects. You may also use a ¼-inch piece of masonite or heavy metal for the front panel. Lay out all the holes as shown in Fig. 5-17.

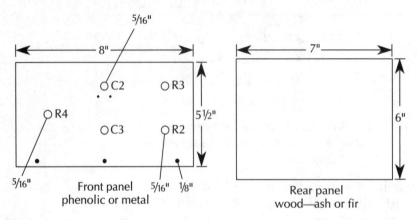

Fig. 5-17   *The layout and dimensions of the front panel. Tape on a sheet of paper with holes to protect the front panel.*

This 5½-×-8-inch panel was cut with a hacksaw. Drill all variable resistance controls with a ⁵⁄₁₆-inch bit. Likewise, drill the hole for capacitor C2, and enlarge it at the back. Make sure both variable capacitors fit flush with the backpanel. Drill ⅛-inch holes for mounting the vernier dial assembly. Place cloth or a towel on each side of the panel so it will not get damaged. Tape the hole layout on the front panel so it will not be scratched while drilling.

After all the holes are drilled and the parts are fitted, wash off the front panel in soapy water. Rinse and thoroughly dry off. Remove all fingerprints and grease marks from the front side. Mark the different controls with white letters and dial transfers. Then spray on a coat of lacquer or acrylic spray. Let it dry several hours. Then cutout and glue a piece of tinfoil on the back using plastic model cement (Fig. 5-18).

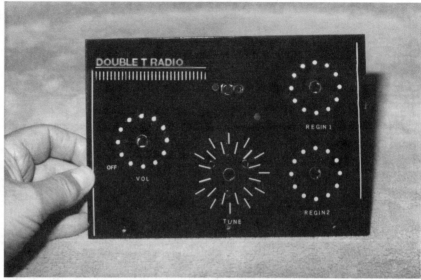

Fig. 5-18 *After all the holes are drilled, clean up the phenolic front and apply dial and number transfers. Spray on a coat of clear lacquer or acrylic spray to protect the markings.*

Make sure the control shafts are not too long. Cut off the C2 shaft if it is. C2 is mounted flush on the back, pushing the vernier dial assembly out in front. This is done to provide a solid capacitor mounting with spacers between the vernier dial assembly and the front panel. If it is not mounted in this way, a larger hole must be drilled to allow both set screws of the venier dial to clear the front panel.

Select the correct size (or cut off larger size) front mounting bolts for both variable air capacitors. If the bolts are too long, it might prevent the rotor plates from rotating, or it could damage the stator plates. These bolts can be ground off or cut with a hacksaw. Always leave a nut on the bolt when cutting or grinding so it will not strip the threads. C3 is a 100-pF variable air capacitor. In this chassis, C3 is in the middle. If a single 100-pF capacitor cannot be found, you can find one in a dual variable capacitor.

Laying out the chassis

You may want to use a metal chassis for the rear instead of a wood chassis. In this project, a small sub-chassis was constructed from a 2¼-x-4-inch piece of double-sided copper PC board which was cut from a larger scrap piece of board. In Fig. 5-19, the 8-pin octal socket for the plug-in coil and a 9-pin socket for Q1 are mounted.

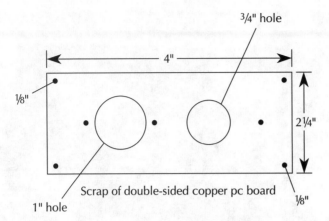

Fig. 5-19 *Layout of the tube and coil sockets on the double-sided PCB.*

Drill a ¾-inch hole for the 9-pin socket and 1-inch hole for the octal tube socket. These holes can be cut with a metal circle cutter or you can drill a bunch of ⅛-inch holes around the outside circle and break out the copper center. You will need to file down the rough edges with a rat-tail file. Drill ⅛-inch holes for mounting the octal tube socket. The 9-pin socket was held in position with epoxy cement. Drill a hole in each corner for mounting the board, and one for the insulated strip. To prevent long coil wire leads, position the octal (coil) socket with pins 1 and 8 pointing towards pins 1 and 2 of the tube socket.

The small transformer can be cemented or bolted to the bottom of the PC board. All small parts on the tube pins can be connected to the insulated strip. Grid coil L1 is soldered to pins 1 and 2, and the tickler coil (L2) winding is wired to 7 and 8. Complete all wiring of the two sockets before mounting them in position on the rear wood chassis.

Building the power supply chassis

One piece of a dual-IC PC board can be used for the power supply chassis (Fig. 5-20). All filter capacitors and diodes can be mounted on the small board. The PCB wiring can be used to connect the voltage-doubler circuit. Solder on extra long leads of hookup wire for the heater leads. Twist these two wires to minimize hum. Use a red flexible lead for the positive voltage, and a black lead for the negative, or ground. Twist together the two ac leads that go to SW1. Dab rubber silicone cement over the soldered switch connections.

Fig. 5-20 *How to mount the power supply parts. The power transformer mounts directly on the wood chassis.*

Notice that only half of the voltage (12.6 V) is fed to the heater pins (4 and 5) of Q1. The same winding is used in the voltage-doubler circuit. Double check the polarity of D1 and D2, C10, C11, and C12. To prevent a shock hazard, make sure that there are no bare wires on the primary or ac power cord connections.

Winding the coils

The three band coil windings are placed on three different coil forms. In the early days, plug-in coils were wound around Bakelite tube sockets. Of course, now these are hard to find, but can be used if you do find them. The three plug-in coils in this project were wound around commercial plug-in forms found in mail-order part suppliers. The plastic forms are 2⁷⁄₁₆ inches long × 1⅜ inches in diameter. They plug into a standard 8-pin octal tube base (Fig. 5-21).

Wind all coils with #24 enameled magnet wire. The windings should be evenly spaced over 1½ inches on the coil form. This means that for the 20-meter band, the grid coil (8 turns) winds over the entire 1½ inches. Place the tickler winding (L2) ⅛ inch away from the grid end (1) of L1. All tickler coils are close wound on the coil form.

Drill very small coil holes at the start and finish of the grid coil. Place two very small holes 1/8 inch away from the grid coil.

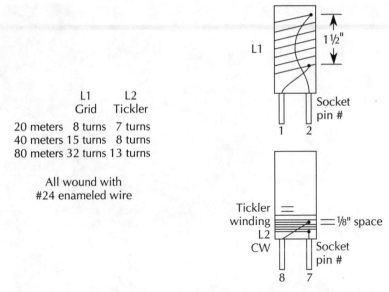

L1   L2
Grid   Tickler

20 meters   8 turns   7 turns
40 meters   15 turns   8 turns
80 meters   32 turns   13 turns

All wound with
#24 enameled wire

Fig. 5-21   *Coil winding for the three bands of 80, 40, and 20 coils.*

The tickler winding is found at the bottom of the coil (Fig. 5-21). Bring the correct grid lead (1) and ground side (2) of L1 to pins 1 and 2, matching the tube socket. The tickler coil windings are soldered to pins 7 and 8. Double check all soldering of coil pins for continuity with the low-ohmmeter range of the multimeter.

Wiring the circuit

First wire the coil tube socket to the 12AT7 tube pins. Make all leads as direct and short as possible. T1 may be cemented or bolted to the double-sided board. Connect all small components on the tube socket board. Run direct hookup wire to C2 and C3. Solder C1 to the antenna lug. Run flexible hookup wire from the copper board to R2, R3, and R4 respectively.

Twist two flexible hookup wires from the power transformer (T2) directly to heater pins 4 and 5. If possible, bring a black and red wire from the dc power supply source. Connect the red wire to the positive terminal of J3 and one side of R3. Tie the black wire to common ground. Double check all your wiring before fastening the chassis to the wood base. To prevent hum, use a small, shielded wire to connect the volume control to the interstage transformer.

Testing the circuit

To test the circuit, simply plug in the 12AT7 tube and the 80-meter coil. Rotate R2 fully and R3 halfway. Plug in a pair of high-impedance headphones. Connect a good antenna and ground wire. Now turn R3 on fully. Rotate regeneration control R3 until oscillations are heard. Tune in C3 until a squeal or a station is heard. Lower R3 to the point of oscillation and slightly decrease R2 until audio is heard.

When C3 is tuned to a group of stations, use the vernier dial and C2 to fine tune each station over the area. Remember to locate the stations first with C3, and then fine tune each station with C2. You may need to reset the regeneration control and R3 after locating a station. Readjustment of C1 may also be needed. Adjust C1 with an insulated tool when the station is tuned in for maximum reception.

Checking the bands

To check the bands, try plugging in the other two coils. If you can borrow a commercial shortwave receiver for a few minutes, you can tell what channel the coil bands are working on. Place the commercial receiver near the regenerative double-T radio and you should hear loud oscillations on the commercial receiver (Fig 5-22). Compare the respective coils to those on the commercial receiver. Remember, shortwave listening is best in the evening and early morning hours.

Start with C3 fully open (not meshed) on each given coil and tune in the coil band heard on the commercial receiver. Tune the

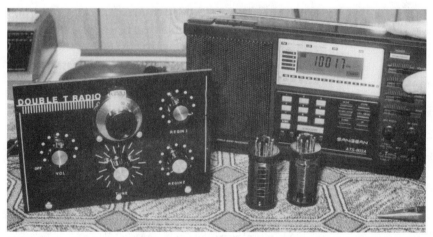

Fig. 5-22 *A commercial shortwave radio is used to determine if each coil is in the right band. Radiation from the regenerative detector is picked up by the commercial receiver.*

commercial receiver until a loud oscillating noise can be heard in the speaker. Now read the band frequency on the commercial receiver. Likewise, check the band with C3 fully meshed. With this method you can determine the total range of frequencies each coil covers. Although the regenerative receiver has great selectivity, it does produce loud oscillations.

Project 4: Toroid coil shortwave radio

What you will need

IC1	ZN414 IC (D.C. Electronics, ZN414 or Circuit Specialists, ZN414)
IC2	LM386 low power IC
C1	365pF variable air capacitor (KA7QJY Components, 365pF or Antique Electronics Supply, CF-230)
C2	15-pF variable air capacitor
C3	0.01-µF, 50-V ceramic capacitor
C4	0.1-µF, 50-V ceramic capacitor
C5, C7	10-µF, 35-V electrolytic capacitor
C6, C8	220-µF, 35-V electrolytic capacitor
C9	0.05-µF, 100-V ceramic capacitor
L1	3 turns of #24 enameled wire, wound over the center of L2
L2	34 turns of #24 enameled wire, wound on T50-2 toroid form
Coil form	Yellow T-50-2 toroid iron core (KA7QJY Components or Oak Hill Research)
R1	100-kilohm, ½-watt resistor
R2	1-kilohm, ½-watt resistor
R3	10-kilohm audio taper control
R4	10 ohm, ½-watt resistor
SW1	Single-pole, double-throw (SPDT) miniature toggle switch
SW2	Double-pole, single-throw (DPST) toggle switch
J1	Stereo headphone jack (Radio Shack 274-247)
B1—B4	Four, 1.5V C-cell batteries (6-V total)
IC socket	8-pin DIP socket for IC2
Cabinet	ABS instrument enclosure 3 × 6 × 6.25 inches (All Electronics Corp., MB-4C)
Misc.	PC board, hookup wire, 4-cell battery holder, 1-cell battery holder knobs, etc.

Most of the receiver circuits using the ZN414 RF IC cover the medium-wave (mw) and long-wave bands (lw). In this project, IC1 operates in the 15- to 18.5-MHz band. Switch SW1 changes the coil from 17 turns to a total of 34 turns. The broadcast shortwave or medium-wave, stations and time station (WWV) can be heard when the coil is tapped at the 17th turn, while CW and hams can be heard when the full winding of the coil is used (Fig. 5-23).

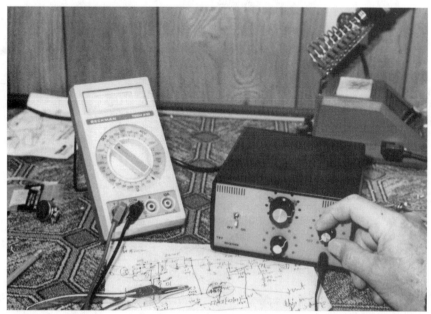

Fig. 5-23   *The experimental toroid coil shortwave radio was built around the Z414 IC and the T50-2 toroid iron core.*

Although winding the coil (L2) with more turns may lower the 19- and 20-meter band, strong local AM stations from 1400 kHz may override the shortwave bands. Double-tuned RF stages could help to eliminate broadcast band interference, but they are expensive and the cost of this shortwave receiver has been kept to a minimum. C2 was added for bandspread but may be eliminated if cost is a factor.

How the circuit works

The outside antenna is coupled to the RF circuit with L1. The outside antenna ground can be connected to the ground side of the input circuit if local broadcast stations at the high end of the broadcast band are not too powerful. It's surprising how many different shortwave stations can be received when you leave the ground off (Fig. 5-24).

SW1 switches in two different bands. L2 is wound with a total of 34 turns of #24 enameled wire on a T-50-2 toroid form. SW1 can switch L2 to the center tap at 17 turns. L1 is 3 turns of the same size wire wound over the center of coil L2. C1 provides station tuning with C2 as the bandspread capacitor.

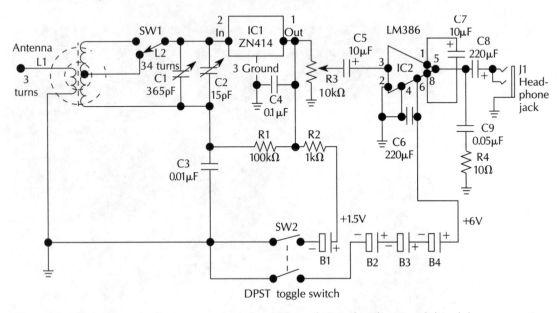

Fig. 5-24 *The schematic diagram consists of an RF tuned IC and audio IC with headphone reception.*

The RF IC contains ten different RF circuits inside a transistor-type case. This three-legged IC has its input at pin 2, its output at 1, and its ground terminal at pin 3. The output audio at pin 1 is fed directly to R3. The volume can be lowered with R3 and capacity-coupled (C5) to pin 3 of IC2.

Although with sufficient volume some of the shortwave stations can be heard, a headphone jack (J1) was installed for quiet listening. Keep C6 as close to pin 6 of IC2 as possible to prevent oscillations. The voltage supply to pin 6 of IC2 is fed from four C cells. IC1 voltage is supplied from the first 1.5-V battery. SW2 is a double-pole, single-throw toggle switch.

Winding the coils

First wind L2 on the ½-inch toroid powdered iron core form with #24 enameled wire. Cut off a piece of magnet wire two feet in length.

Insert wire through the center and pull each winding tight. The coil wire is fairly self-supporting, and when wound tight around the iron core will stay there. Twist the wire about six times at the 17th turn. Wind on another 17 turns making a total of 34 turns (Fig. 5-25).

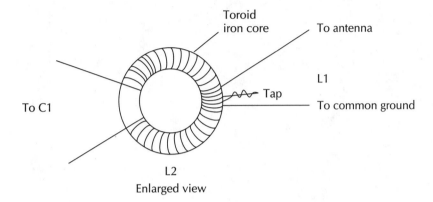

L1—3 turns of #24 enameled magnet wire wound over center of L2.
L2—34 turns of #24 enameled wire—coils wound on toroid iron core form T-50-2—tapped at the 17th turn. Form has only 1/2-inch diameter.

Fig. 5-25   *Wind 34 turns, with a tap at the 17th turn, for L2 on the small 1/2-inch diameter iron core form.*

Place L1 over the center of L2. Wind half of the coil on one side of the tap, and the other half on the other side for a total of three turns. Pull the wire tight so it lies between the turns of L2. Clean off the enamel coating with a pocket knife. Tin each soldered lead with flux and solder. Use a 150-watt soldering iron, if possible, to melt off the enamel and make a good solder connection. The coil form lays flat against the etched PCB and requires no cement to hold it in position.

Building the PC board

This shortwave receiver fits inside an instrument enclosure. The 3-inch plastic front cover is removed, and the etched PC chassis slides down into the grooved area of the enclosure. This serves as both the front panel and the component chassis. All parts are mounted on the PCB except for the flashlight batteries (Fig. 5-26).

Both variable capacitors are mounted in the center of the PCB. If larger variable capacitors are used, you may need a larger cabinet, or you may need to change the PC wiring. Large variable capacitors can short the PC wiring since they are mounted flat

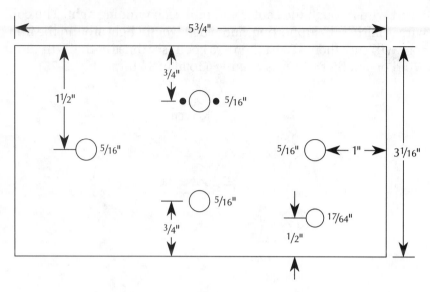

Fig. 5-26 *Layout of the Front panel dimensions.*

against it. If this is the case, move the horizontal ground and the audio PC wiring out of the way. You may want to place plastic insulators between the variable capacitors and the board.

First lay out the PCB wiring. The variable capacitors, volume control, and SW1 mounting holes can be drilled through the copper side before etching (Fig. 5-27). Parts layout is not too critical, except you need to keep the RF circuits to the left of the board, and audio components to the right of the board. PCB wiring can be etched in 30 to 45 minutes if the etching tray is rocked during the process.

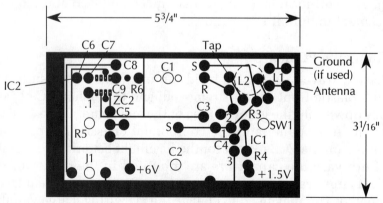

Fig. 5-27 *The PCB mounts all the small components on the etched wiring side.*

Mounting parts

All parts, except the battery holder, mount on the front panel as surface-mounted components. Small resistor and capacitor leads are cut short with an L-bent soldered lead. These leads hold the parts in place and are soldered directly onto the PCB wiring.

Before mounting parts, you might want to apply letter and dial transfers to the clean PCB surface. These should be rubbed on before large parts are mounted. Do not spray on clear lacquer, varnish, or acrylic spray until the wiring is completed as the heat from the soldering could melt or mar the lettering. Spray on the clear finish once the set is built and you know it works.

First mount the IC socket. Bend all 8-pin terminals flat against the PCB and solder directly on the wiring. Twist the outside leads to match the PCB wiring. If pin 1 is not marked, mark it now. Next, solder all small components as they are mounted onto the PCB.

Cut the leads of the small coil short after mounting. SW1 can be mounted with bare hookup wire from each terminal to the PCBwiring. Next, mount the variable capacitors and extend their leads to the PCB wiring. All the ground leads (rotor) of the capacitors can be soldered together. Connect bare lead wires to the volume control and solder it to the PCB (Fig. 5-28).

Fig. 5-28 *The parts are mounted on the rear of the PCB, and the knobs are mounted on the outside. The PCB slides down inside the front panel groove areas.*

Connecting the batteries

Select four C-cell battery holders with leads. Connect a long lead from the black or negative lead between the first battery and ground. No soldering is needed because the battery springs hold the lug between the positive connection of the B1 cell and the negative one of the B2 cell. This 1.5-volt lead is soldered to the 1.5-VPCB wiring (Fig. 5-29).

Fig. 5-29 *Back view of a completed board with all parts mounted and soldered.*

Testing the circuit

The receiver is ready for a trial run after all the parts are mounted and soldered into position. Turn the volume control fully on. It's best to try out this shortwave radio late at night or early in the morning, when shortwave signals are strongest. Of course, reception will depend on where you live. Reception tends to be better at both coasts.

Rotate C1 to tune in a station. You will notice that the highest frequencies come in with only a small portion of C1 meshed. Try each band for reception. The outside antenna must be connected for good shortwave reception. Connect a ground lead if strong local broadcasts are not located at the high end of the regular broadcast band. The ground is connected to the circuit through a variable air capacitor, with a range between 50 to 100 pF. This can help your reception, and help knock out strong local broadcast stations.

Although simple in design, this radio picked up long distant international stations. Larger areas of the band range may be picked up by tapping the 17th turn of coil L2, and by using a rotary selection switch. If local broadcast stations at the high end of the dial drown out other stations, add the trap circuit shown in Fig. 5-30 to tune these stations out. This trap can be built on a separate PCB, grid board, or perfboard.

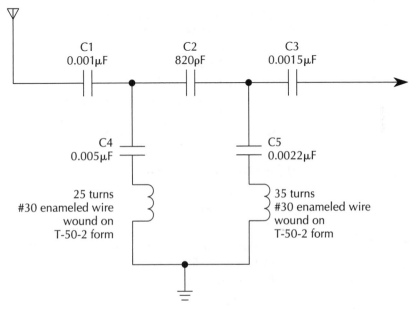

Fig. 5-30 *Add a trap circuit if broadcast stations above 1400 kHz try to come in. Place the trap in series with the antenna lead.*

Project 5: Two-band direct-conversion radio

What you will need

C1	0.01-µF, 50-volt ceramic capacitor
C2, C3, C4	100-pF, 50-volt silver mica capacitor
C5, C9, C12	220-µF, 35-volt electrolytic capacitor
C6	5–20-pF variable capacitor with 7:1 reduction gear assembly (KA7QJY Components)
C7, C11	0.1-µF, 50-volt ceramic capacitor

C13	0.05-µF, 50-volt ceramic capacitor
R1	1-kilohm, ½-watt resistor
R2	10-ohm, ½-watt resistor
R3	10-kilohm audio taper control with switch
T1, T2	Shielded coils (Amidon, L57-6 or Ocean State Electronics, L45-7-PCT-B-4 coil forms)
IC1	NE-602 IC (D.C. Electronics, NE-602)
IC2	LM386 IC
B1	9-volt battery
J1	Metal antenna jack (Radio Shack, 274-346)
J2	$\frac{3}{32}$-inch stereo headphone jack
SW1	Single-pole, single throw (SPST) switch on rear of R3
2	8-pin IC DIP sockets
1	9-volt battery holder (Radio Shack, 270-326)
Cabinet	metal (D.C. Electronics, 463N or Hosfelt Electronics TG-36)
Misc.	PC board, solder, flexible hookup wire, etc.

What you will need for the bandpass filter

3	0.001-µF, 50-volt ceramic capacitor
1	33-pF, 50-volt ceramic capacitor
1	0.006-µF, 50-volt ceramic capacitor
L1, L2	30 turns of #30 enameled wire, wound on a toroid iron core form (T-50-2)
1	1-x-2-inch piece of perfboard

This shortwave receiver pulls in international broadcasting stations on the 19-meter band and amateur radio operators (or ham operators) on the 20-meter band. The ham band is picked up from 14,165 kHz to 14,350 kHz, and the international stations are received for up to 15,500 kHz with the variable capacitor fully rotated. You can adjust the oscillator coil (L2) to cover only the international broadcast band, if desired (Fig. 5-31).

This small shortwave receiver should be enclosed in a metal cabinet to prevent outside noise from interfering with the broadcast stations. To eliminate interference from the stations in the ham range, a built-in 6:1 or 7:1 reduction variable capacitor or vernier dial drive assembly must be used. Slowing the rotation of the small variable capacitor provides pin-point tuning.

To prevent local broadcast stations from being picked up, a high bandpass filter network is constructed on a piece of perf-

Fig. 5-31   *This direct-conversion shortwave receiver pulls in ham and international broadcast stations on the 19- and 20-meter band.*

board. If desired, this bandpass circuit can be placed on the same PCB chassis as the rest of the radio by enlarging the PCB. The bandpass circuit is inserted between J1 and antenna input of T1.

How the circuit works

The two-band direct-conversion shortwave receiver uses only two IC components for headphone reception. Mixer and oscillator (NE 602) IC1 operates as the RF circuit, mixer, and direct-conversion oscillator. A balanced front end and coil (T1) provide broadband RF amplification. No tuning capacitor is needed in this circuit. T2 acts as a variable frequency oscillator (VFO) in the direct-conversion circuit.

The Signetics NE-602 IC (IC1) is a low-powered monolithic double-balanced mixer with input amplifier, on-board oscillator, and voltage regulator (Fig. 5-32). Although the NE-602 was originally designed for cellular phone operation, it works well in this shortwave circuit. It can oscillate for a frequency of up to 200

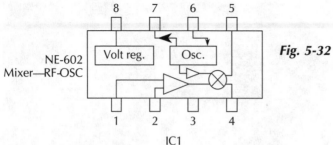

Fig. 5-32 *The NE-602 mixer, oscillator, and RF circuit IC works great in the direct-conversion SW receiver.*

MHz in a crystal oscillator circuit, tuned-tank oscillator, or an external buffer oscillator.

The audio output from pin 4 of IC1 is connected to volume control R3. Op amp (operational amplifier), IC2 (LM386) provides the volume for headphone operation (Fig. 5-33). Output audio at pin 5 of IC2 is capacitance-coupled to the headphone jack (J2).

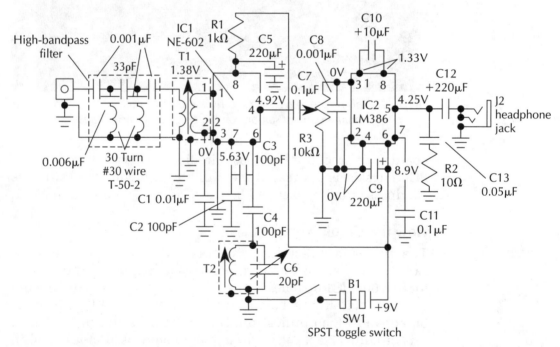

Fig. 5-33 *The schematic includes a high bandpass filter network and broadband RF stage in conjunction with the NE-602 IC. Headphone operation is provided by a low-powered IC (LM386).*

Because this receiver pulls only a small amount of current (8.3 to 21.7 mA), it is easily operated from a 9-volt battery. The current rises in direct proportion to the volume control. Nine volts is applied to IC2 at pin 6, and to pin 8 of IC1 through R2 (1-kilohm) resistor. IC1 should not operate above a maximum of 8 volts dc. Resistor R2 drops the voltage to 5.8 volts dc.

Winding the coils

It's difficult to obtain small, shielded shortwave coils for a shortwave set today. It may be necessary to wind them yourself. Actually, it's easy to wind #30 enameled wire on a slotted plastic bobbin.

Choose either two L57-6 Amidon coil forms or Ocean State L45-7-PCT-B-4 coil forms. These are shielded coil forms that come apart. These shielded coil forms have a frequency range of 1 to 20 MHz (Fig. 5-34).

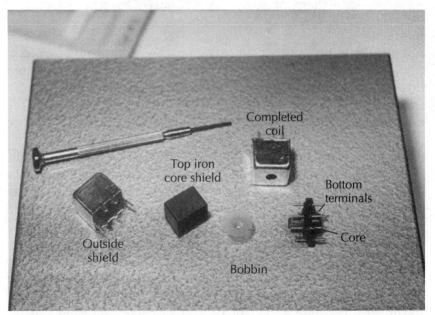

Fig. 5-34 *T1 & T2 are hand-wound shielded coils, wound on a small plastic bobbin.*

Simply bend back the mounting tabs and remove the bottom lead connections. You will see the small plastic bobbin that you will wind your coil on. This fits in a slot at the bottom of the coil. Both T1 and T2 are wound with #30 enameled magnet wire, which is readily available at mail-order stores.

Wind 15 turns of wire on the plastic bobbin. Leave about 1 inch of excess wire for soldering. The 15 turns you have wound fills up the first layer of coil. Cut a piece of transparent tape about ¼ inch wide and ½ inch long. Place tape over the first layer

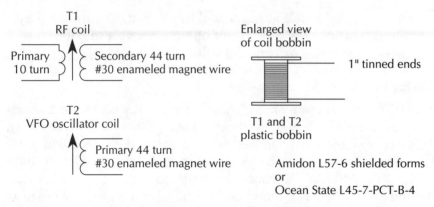

Fig. 5-35 *Wind on 44 turns of #30 enameled wire for the secondary of T1, and 10 turns for the primary winding. T2 has only 44 turns total of the same size wire.*

of coil. Wind on another 15 turns for the second layer. Again, place tape between coil layers. Wind on 14 turns for the final layer of coil, making a total of 44 turns (Fig. 5-35).

It's wise to cut the pieces of tape before winding the coil. Try not to overlap coil windings at any time. Place them side by side and make sure they are close wound. The tape provides an even coil winding and holds the coil in position.

Now place another layer of tape over the finished winding to hold it in place, and to provide a smooth winding area for the primary winding of T1. Wind on 10 turns of #30 enameled wire over the secondary winding. Tape the final winding. Leave 1 inch of wire on each coil end for connections.

Scrape off the enamel coating at each coil end. Tin the fine wire with solder. Check the continuity of both windings with the low-range setting of the ohmmeter. The secondary coil will have the greatest resistance. Use the two outside leads on each side for solder connections. After it is soldered, double check wire continuity with an ohmmeter.

Wind the tinned primary leads around opposite coil pins and solder. You need only a little solder. If too much solder is used, the metal ferrite shield will not fit down over the connections. Once again, check both coils for continuity after the connections are soldered. Place a white or black dot on the secondary winding side for easy identification when mounting. Liquid correction fluid (typewriter) is ideal for this.

Bend the top of each terminal slightly inward towards the coil bobbin. This ensures the coil winding will not short against the powdered skirt or coil shield. Now bend the small bottom tabs of the shield to hold the entire coil assembly. Adjust the alignment screw so that it is flush with the bottom of the plastic form.

Now, wind the oscillator coil (T2). This coil is 44 turns, and is wound the same as T1, except that it has no primary winding. The variable-frequency oscillator coil is wound in three different layers and marked the same as T1. T2 is tuned with a variable capacitor (5 pF to 20 pF) with a built-in 7:1 reduction shaft. Always check for continuity of each winding after the coil is completely assembled.

Laying out the PC board

Saw a 3-×-2-inch piece of PCB from a larger piece with a hacksaw or saber saw. Grind or sand down rough edges. File off each foil edge with a flat file. Wash off the copper side with soap and water.

Lay out the PC wiring as shown in Fig. 5-36. Keep both IC sockets in the center of the PCB. Coils T1 and T2 are mounted on each side of IC1. Keep the shielded coils towards the outside edge of the PCB. Mark pin 1 of each IC with a dot.

Small components can be mounted between the IC sockets and shielded coils. Keep all coil leads as short as possible. Double check the PC wiring before etching the board. Again inspect the board for poorly etched wiring after the etching process.

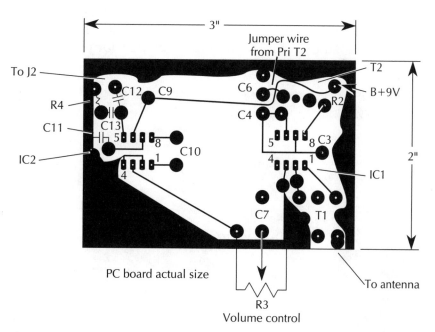

Fig. 5-36 *Cut a piece of copper PCB 2 × 3 inches from a larger piece. Lay out the parts using this actual size drawing.*

Drill all the small mounting holes with the smallest bit possible. A ⅟₁₆-inch bit is found in most PCB etching kits. Drill a ¼-inch mounting hole in each corner of the board. Also drill a ¼-inch screwdriver hole in the center of T1 and T2 for coil adjustment. Drill a larger hole in the center if the plastic slug assembly protrudes above the surface mount.

Mounting parts

First mount the IC1 and IC2 sockets. Be sure that no two terminals are soldered together. Run a knife blade between each pin terminal to remove excess solder or rosin. Check socket connections with a magnifying glass to be sure good solder joints have been made. Test each connection for continuity between the top of the socket and the wiring on the bottom of the PCB with the low-ohm setting of an ohmmeter.

Next mount T1 and T2. Make sure the primary and secondary sides are connected correctly. If the secondary winding was marked, make sure both secondary windings face toward the IC1 socket. The primary winding of both coils are on the outside near common ground. Solder the coil shield tabs to common ground.

When mounting the electrolytic capacitors, be sure to observe correct polarity. Mount the small resistors and bypass capacitors last. For stability, choose silver mica capacitors for C3, C4, and C6. Push capacitors against the PCB and solder. Place a white dot or felt pen marking on top of the PCB for pin 1 of both IC1 and IC2 (Fig. 5-37).

Fig. 5-37 *Closeup showing the small components mounted on the PCB.*

Tuning the circuit

To align T1 and T2, leave the iron core of T1 in the middle of the coil, and the core of T2 flush with the bottom of the plastic core. T1 and T2 can be aligned with an RF signal generator, frequency meter, or you can borrow another shortwave receiver from a friend.

If you borrow another receiver, tune the borrowed set at 19 meters. Then place your two-band receiver near the plastic case. If the borrowed receiver has a plastic case and has calibrated frequencies, so much the better (Fig. 5-38). You should hear a whistle in the borrowed receiver when the variable capacitor (C6) is rotated. Leave the cover off the metal cabinet.

Fig. 5-38 *You can align the variable-frequency oscillator (VFO) by removing the metal cover from a second SW receiver and placing it next to the VFO. Whistling noises caused by the VFO in the second receiver indicate the exact frequency.*

Rotate the two-band receiver to the high end (with the capacitor plates almost fully out), and you can hear the oscillating signal on the borrowed SW radio. Notice the frequency of setting. Now rotate C6 until all plates are meshed. Check the whistle frequency on the borrowed receiver. Adjust the core of T2 so that the ham radio band begins when the plates on C6 are meshed (14,165 kHz). Now, check to see if the international radio broadcast bands are heard at the high end of the dial with the C6 plates opened (15,500 kHz).

Adjust T1 for maximum volume of ham or radio stations. If you do not want to listen to the ham bands, adjust T2 so that you can hear the full range of the international broadcast stations (15,100 to 15,500 kHz). Always use a plastic adjustment tool when adjusting the iron core so you don't damage it.

You can also tune in WWV at 15,000 kHz, which is right in the middle of the dial. If it is not right in the middle, adjust T2 until it is. Now, the ham bands should be at the low end of the dial, and international broadcast stations cover the rest. Readjust T1 for maximum reception.

Testing the circuit

To test the circuit, first connect flexible hookup wire to the variable capacitor (C6), volume control (R3), and battery cable. Plug in the 9-volt battery. Plug in the outdoor antenna at J1 and headphones at J2. Insert each IC into their respective sockets. Be sure pin 1 is inserted in the correct position in the socket. Rotate the volume control halfway up, and rotate the variable capacitor until you hear whistling. Tune in the international broadcast stations at the high end, and the ham bands at the low end when the variable capacitor plates are almost meshed.

Remember that each whistle you hear is a station. Fine tune each station with the large variable capacitor knob. Carefully tune the VFO signal against the incoming signal until audio is heard. International broadcasts are easily tuned in. Single sideband (SSB) ham signals require careful tuning to hear clear voices. After you've tuned in a few amateur stations, the next time will be easy.

Troubleshooting

What happens if the radio does not make a sound when the switch is turned on? First, check the audio output stages. Place a screwdriver blade at the top of the volume control and listen for a loud hum. If you hear no hum or clicks, check the audio stages. Check voltages on IC2 and compare them to the schematic (Fig. 5-39).

Low voltage can indicate that an electrolytic capacitor is in backwards, that the power output IC is in backwards, that there is a voltage leak between the IC terminals, or that you have a defective component. Remove the battery from the set. If the volt-

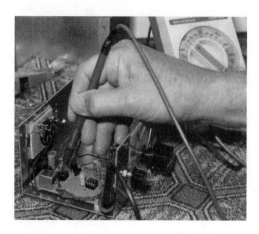

Fig. 5-39 *Take voltage measurements with the DMM and compare your readings with those found on the schematic.*

age is low on certain terminals, check with 2-kilohm range on the ohmmeter. Clean out any solder spills between each IC pin with a pocket knife.

If the audio is normal, but no stations can be tuned in, check that IC1 is not installed in the socket wrong. Look for a pin not plugged into the socket. Measure the voltage on each pin and compare it to the schematic. Also look for a broken wire on variable capacitor C6. Look for poorly soldered connections on components.

Building the AM station attenuator circuit

To stop AM broadcast stations from blocking out all the shortwave stations, a simple high bandpass filter circuit can be added before the antenna input. This circuit consists of ceramic bypass capacitors and two coils wound on toroid-powdered iron core forms (Fig. 5-40). L1 and L2 are wound on a separate T50-2 (red) toroid form. Both coils are wound with # 30 enameled magnet wire.

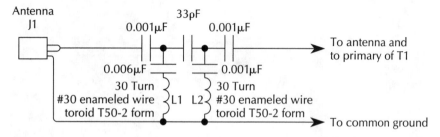

Fig. 5-40 *If strong local stations drown out other stations, insert this high bandpass circuit between antenna J1 and T1.*

Cut a small piece (1 × 2 inches) of perfboard from a larger piece. All connections need to be made as short as possible. Thread each coil wire through the small holes in the form to prevent the coils from unwinding. Cement the coil forms to the perfboard with a bit of silicone rubber cement. Mount the small components on one side, and solder the connections on the opposite side.

Connect a piece of flexible hookup wire for the input and output antenna connections. Keep all leads as short as possible. Solder leads to the antenna input jack and ground lug. Tie both ground and antenna connections to the receiver PCB.

Final note

Place the shortwave chassis and battery in a metal cabinet. In Fig. 5-41, you'll see we used a grey LMB 463-N small metal cabinet. Drill a ¼-inch hole in the rear metal plate for antenna jack J1. Place a large knob on a reduction shaft for easier tuning. Keep the leads on C6 as short as possible.

This SW receiver was easy to build, picks up an amazing number of SW stations with the outside antenna. C8 can be re-

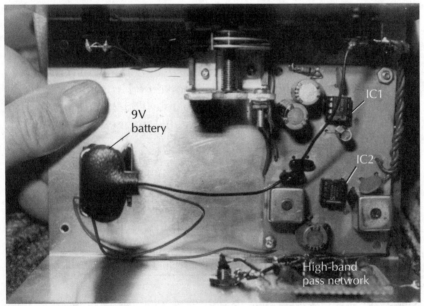

Fig. 5-41 *The small SW receiver completely wired and ready to go. Placement of components is not too critical.*

moved for more volume if strong shortwave stations are not heard. With this direct-conversion receiver, you do not need an additional beat-frequency oscillator (BFO) for the SSB bands.

The best time for SSB reception is early in the morning. The high bandpass filter network can be eliminated if there are no high-powered AM stations in your area. In this case, just connect the primary winding of T1 to the antenna post and to ground.

Tuning is very delicate with a direct-conversion receiver. Tune for the null point between whistles on the broadcast (international) band. For ham stations, tune until voices are clear. Direct-conversion radio is ideal for continuous wave (CW) reception. Keep the volume control set low at all times.

Project 6: A simple superhet radio

What you will need

IC1	NE 602 integrated circuit
IC2	ZN414 integrated circuit (D.C. Electronics or Circuit Specialists)
IC3	LM386 integrated circuit
C1, C3, C5	0.001-µF, 50-volt ceramic capacitor
C2 5pf	Silver mica capacitor
C4	0.006-µF, 50-volt ceramic or paper capacitor
C6,	0.01-µF, 50-volt ceramic capacitor
C7, C8, C9	100-pF silver mica capacitor
C10	15-pF or 18-pF variable air capacitor (KA7QJY Components or Ocean State Electronics, HF-15 or Oak Hill Research AV03)
C11, C17, C19	220-µF, 35-volt electrolytic capacitor
C12, C13, C14, C15, C18	0.1-µF, 50-volt ceramic capacitor
C16	10-µF, 35-volt electrolytic capacitor
C20	0.05-µF, 50-volt ceramic capacitor
R1	1-kilohm linear variable control
R2	470-ohm, ½-watt resistor
R3, R6	1-kilohm, ½-watt resistor
R4	100-kilohm ½-watt resistor
R5	3.8-kilohm, ½-watt resistor
R7	10-kilohm, ½-watt resistor

R8	10-kilohm volume control taper with a switch (SW1)
R9	10-ohm, ½-watt resistor
T1	12 turns of #30 enameled magnet wire, 67 turns #30 enameled magnet wire on secondary winding
T2	72 turns #30 enameled magnet wire
2	Shielded coil forms
Vernier dial assembly	6:1 or 8:1, 1½-inch vernier dial with 0–10 markings (Oak Hills Research, Ocean State Electronics, VD112-10, or D.C. Electronics, #45KN100)
FL1	455-kHz ceramic filter network (DigiKey, #TK2330 4-kHz bandwidth or D.C. Electronics, #CFU445D)
J1	Panel mount (Radio Shack, 274-346)
J2	Headphone jack (Radio Shack, 274-247)
B1	9-V battery
SW1	Single-pole, single throw (SPST) switch on back of R5
Cabinet	Metal, (Hosfelt Electronics or D.C. Electronics, #463N
Misc.	Two 8-pin IC DIP sockets, 9-volt battery, battery holder, screws & bolts, solder, etc.

You can build a simple superhet shortwave receiver to work in the range of 30 to 40 MHz. If you desire the ham radio band (7000–7300 kHz) and the international broadcasting band (7100–7500 kHz), you rotate the variable frequency oscillator (VFO) coil slug in. To get the 30-meter band, you back the oscillator coil out. The VFO coil and a 15–20-pF variable air capacitor tunes in the stations (Fig. 5-42).

How the circuit works

The simple superhet circuit consists of a high bandpass filter network, untuned RF, VFO and mixer, a 455-kHz filter network, an intermediate frequency-automatic gain control IC, and audio output IC circuits (Fig. 5-43).

Fig. 5-42 *This small superhet shortwave receiver uses only three small IC components with headphone reception.*

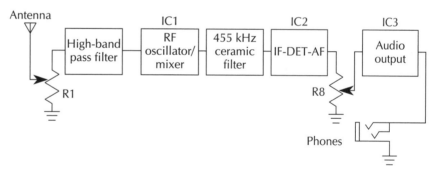

Fig. 5-43 *A block diagram of the various stages and IC components within the radio.*

The antenna input circuit contains a 1-kilohm control to prevent overloading, and a high bandpass filter network to eliminate strong local broadcast stations from drowning out the shortwave bands. The filter network in this project is constructed on the same PC board, but they could be mounted on a separate PC board or perfboard. If there are no high-powered broadcast stations at the high end of band in your area, you can leave off the high bandpass filter.

The primary of T1 connects to the antenna input, and the secondary winding applies RF signal to pins 1 and 2 of IC1. The T1 slug is adjusted for maximum reception. The input RF circuit is untuned to eliminate using another variable capacitor. This superhet circuit was designed to be as simple and inexpensive as possible.

The VFO circuit is tuned by C10 and T2. Notice that T2 has only a single winding and is coupled to the mixer circuit of IC1 with C9. Capacitors C7, C8, and C9 should be silver mica or NPO ceramic disc capacitors with 5 or 10 percent tolerance (Fig. 5-44).

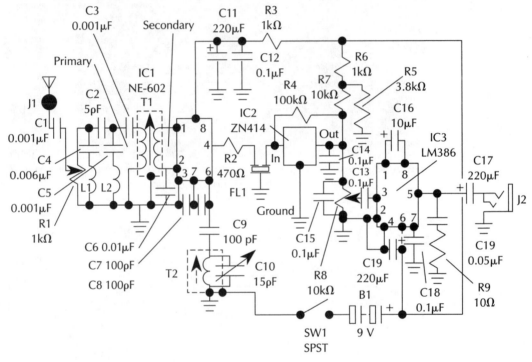

Fig. 5-44 *The main wiring schematic showing the high bandpass filter inserted between the antenna and the RF coil (T1).*

The intermediate frequency (IF) is taken from pin 4 of IC1 to a ceramic filter (455 kHz) IF component. This IF signal is coupled to IC2, which is an RF IC amplifier with detection and audio output circuits. R6 controls the audio applied to output IC3 (LM386). The circuit has plenty of volume for the headphones.

A single 9-volt battery operates this SW superhet receiver. In fact, a nickel-cadmium battery was used so that it could be recharged. Pin 8 of IC1 is fed through filter network R2 and C11. IC1 should operate below a maximum of 8 volts dc.

Winding the coils

Use a shielded coil form with a plastic bobbin to wind the coils. Remove the plastic bobbin and wind on 67 turns of #30 enameled magnet wire for the secondary of T2. Start wrapping the wire around the slot in the bobbin to prevent it from turning. Wind on 15 turns to fill the area. Place a thin piece of tape over the winding. Cut the tape pieces to the width of the bobbin. Keep on winding another layer of 15 turns until the total secondary winding is complete. The tape used between the windings keeps the coil winding uniform, plus you can see how many turns of wire are on each layer (Fig. 5-45).

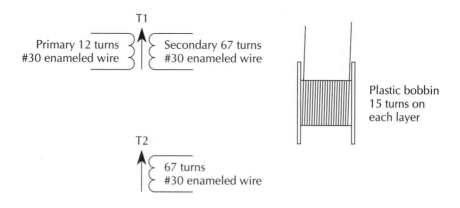

Place secondary winding on first layer of Scotch tape.
Place primary winding over secondary with T1.

Fig. 5-45   *Coil layouts showing the total number of windings for T1 and T2.*

Wind on another layer of 15 turns and a layer of tape until all 67 turns are in place. The top layer will have a total of 7 turns. Place a thin piece of tape over the winding to hold them in position. Then place 12 turns of #30 enameled wire over this winding for the primary winding of T1.

Finally, place a layer of tape over the final winding of T1. Notice that the bobbin is almost full. Put the bobbin back in the shielded form. Wrap the leads and check the continuity of the wires with the low-ohm range of an ohmmeter.

Scrape off the enamel from the wire and tin each 1-inch length of wire. Wrap the respective secondary winding wires around the small terminal posts. Mark the secondary winding with white correction fluid or enamel paint to make it easier to identify the two windings after the outside shield is replaced.

Next, wrap primary wires around the terminal posts. Solder each terminal. Melt off any excess solder, and bend the terminal, post inward so it does not short against the iron shield. Replace the metal sleeve and the outside metal shield. Again, check each winding for continuity with an ohmmeter. Make sure the shield is not grounded against one of the terminal posts. T1 is ready to be mounted.

The VFO coil (T2) is wound in the same manner. Wind 67 turns of #30 enameled wire. This oscillator coil has only one winding. Mount and solder the plastic bobbin, as you did for T1. Double check coil continuity. Mount the metal and outside shield over the coil. Bend over the metal shield tabs to hold the coil assembly together. Mark the oscillator coil on the outside so it will not get installed in the wrong place on the PCB. Adjust the slug in T2 so each is even with the bottom plastic mounting piece.

Laying out the PC board

Cut a piece of PCB 3½ × 2½ inches. Square all four sides and smooth any rough edges with a sander. Also use a file for a smoother edge. Follow the PCB layout in Fig. 5-46. IC1 is mounted in the center of the board, with the audio output IC to the extreme bottom left corner. The filter network is mounted at the top left corner on the PC layout wiring.

After drilling all component holes with a ⅟₁₆-inch drill bit, drill out the center coil holes with a ⁵⁄₁₆-inch bit so the plastic hub mounts flat against the PCB. You might have to enlarge each coil hole terminal until the coil assembly is flush against the board. Make sure both IC socket holes are exact before starting to mount any components. Drill a ⁵⁄₃₂-inch hole in each corner of the PCB for easy mounting.

Mounting parts

To mount parts, first mount the 8-pin DIP sockets because they are difficult to solder. Bend over each tab. Solder each pin with a small amount of solder. Check each soldered pin connection with a magnifying glass. Double check that each soldered connection is to the correct tap pin. Check each pin with the low-ohm range of an ohmmeter. Clean out between the pin connections with a pocket knife or a small screwdriver blade.

Next mount both shielded coils. Make sure T2 is mounted as the VFO coil. Place it on the PCB with the white marking on the bottom towards the IC1 socket. This coil has the most resistance (around 1

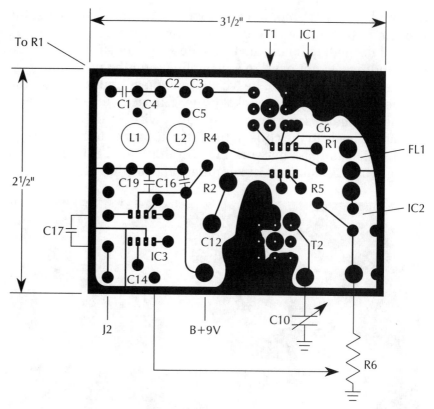

Fig. 5-46 *PCB layout with all parts except C10, J1, J2, and 9-volt battery mounted on the board.*

ohm). Check each soldered pin to ensure it has a good connection. The outside center tab of each coil is soldered to ground.

Mount and solder in all other small components. Since IC2 has terminals like a transistor, install this last and use a pair of long-nose pliers as a heat sink. Be careful not to apply too much heat. Double check all wiring connections with a magnifying glass to be sure no two wires are soldered together.

Building the high bandpass filter network

High bandpass filter parts can be mounted directly on the PCB. Mount all the small components, and then wind the small toroid coils.

Cut off a piece of #30 enameled wire 1½ feet long. Select a T50-2 or similar toroid coil form. Start by holding 1½-inch length under your thumb. Feed the wire end up through the hole in the toroid form. Remember that each time the wire enters this inside area, it's considered one turn. Pull the wire tight, and slide the turn under your thumb. Keep the wire taut. Keep repeating this process until 30 turns are counted. Again, use the magnifying glass, if needed, to count the turns. Be sure there are no kinks in the winding. Do not overlap a turn of wire on the winding.

Cut off each end wire. Leave a ¾-inch piece and scrape off the enameled coating with a pocket knife. Tin each wire end. L1 and L2 should be the same amount of turns with similar windings. Solder the leads to the coils in the filter network on the PCB (Fig. 5-47). This bandpass network may be eliminated if there are no strong broadcast stations in your area (above 1400 kHz).

Fig. 5-47 *Closeup of all parts mounted on the PCB, and ready to be placed in the cabinet.*

Aligning the receiver

Aligning the RF, oscillator, and IF sections is pretty simple. Start with both RF and oscillator coils flush with the bottom of the plastic coil form. No IF alignment is needed since the 455-kHz ceramic filter is a fixed frequency.

Start your alignment with the oscillator coil (T2). Set the variable capacitor so that all the rotor plates are meshed. Rotate the oscillator slug about one full turn. Now check for ham stations with the variable capacitor set so that the rotor is about ⅓ out of the stator plates. If you can hear talking, but it is not clear, the frequency range should be about 7100 to 7900 kHz with full rotation of the variable capacitor (C10). Adjust RF coil T1 for maximum reception with the station tuned in (Fig. 5-48).

Fig. 5-48 *Adjust the oscillator coil (T1) for the tuning band, and coil T2 for maximum reception. No IF alignment is required.*

If you desire more of the international broadcast band, rotate C10 until the rotor plates just enter the stator plates. Adjust the oscillator slug (T2) out until you can hear the National Bureau of Standards station (WWV) at 10,000 kHz. The variable capacitor will tune the entire international band from 10,000 kHz to 9300 kHz. Higher frequencies can be obtained by rotating the slug out of coil T2.

Laying out the front panel

The SW superhet should be placed in a metal cabinet to help keep out interference and strong broadcast stations. Since this small radio only has one IF stage, interference can be a problem.

The RF and volume control with vernier (VFO) tuning dial assembly is mounted on the front panel. J2 is centered at the bottom with the vernier dial directly above it. Use a fairly large (⁷⁄₁₆-inch) bit for the vernier dial assembly (Fig. 5-49).

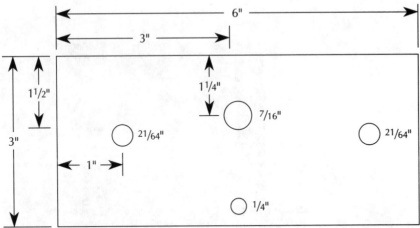

Fig. 5-49 *Layout of the various holes to be drilled in the front panel of the metal cabinet.*

Select a ²¹⁄₆₄-inch bit for both the volume controls. Drill a ¼-inch-bit hole for the headphone jack. Drill three ¹¹⁄₆₄-bit holes to hold the dial assembly to the front panel. Drill a ¼-inch hole in the top rear panel for the antenna jack (J1).

The variable capacitor (C10) mounts on a separate bracket at the rear of the vernier dial assembly. Cut the metal bracket just wide enough for the variable capacitor mounting holes. One bolt and nut can hold the bracket to the bottom of the cabinet. Set in the small chassis and drill corner holes so the PCB can be mounted up from the metal bottom with plastic spacers. Be sure to align the shaft of C10 correctly with the vernier dial, or the dial assembly could slip and the capacitor will not turn.

Testing the circuit

The circuit should be tested and aligned with the PCB out of the metal cabinet. Alignment can be touched up after it is mounted in the case. Make sure all wires are properly connected. Use shielded cable between the volume control and the *out* terminal of IC2, and to C14 at the input of IC3. Also, connect shielded cable to the antenna input from control R1.

After inserting the 9-volt battery, turn SW1 on with the volume halfway up. Right away, with antenna connected, you should hear some RF noise. Rotate the vernier dial to pick up stations. The ham stations will be clustered together and you will hear whistling and garbled voices.

If you do not hear sound, place a small screwdriver tip to the center terminal of the volume control. You should hear hum. If you do not, take voltage measurements on IC3, and compare them to the voltages, on the wiring schematic. Double check the headphone jack, that IC3 is inserted into the socket correctly, and measure to see if too much current is being drawn. Set the digital multimeter to the 20-mA scale, and with SW1 turned off, measure the operating current across the switch terminals. The correct current range for SW1 is 10–36 mA. If too much current is being drawn, the 9-volt battery voltage will rapidly decrease. Suspect a leaky IC3 (LM386) or incorrect wiring connection (Fig. 5-50).

Fig. 5-50 *Checking the normal operating current across SW1 with the switch turned off.*

If you hear no stations, or not even any oscillations, suspect IC1. Place a screwdriver blade to the input pin (2) of IC2. You should hear a rushing noise. Take voltage measurements on the pins of IC2 and compare them to the schematic. Local radio stations can be heard if the screwdriver blade is touched to the filter network's (FL1), *in* and *out* terminals.

The oscillator can be checked by placing another shortwave receiver close to the variable capacitor. Wrap a small piece of wire on the antenna terminal of an external SW receiver, and tune to the operating shortwave band. Lay the antenna wire near C10. Rotate C10 and listen for a loud whistle in the SW receiver. Make sure the volume is turned up. You can tell if the VFO is operating within the correct shortwave band with this test.

In the late evening and early morning hours, the shortwave bands are full of stations. Listen to the excitement of international broadcasts, foreign broadcasts, and amateur radio operators with this simple superhet SW receiver. Happy listening!

❖6

Special receiver projects

YOU WILL FIND A VARACTOR-TUNED RADIO, A TWO-BAND IC RADIO, an IC speaker radio, a radio made from surplus parts, and a solar cell radio in this chapter. You can hear world news, religious stations, music, foreign stations, and ham and regular broadcast stations on the various receivers you will build.

Project 1: 15-MHz varactor-tuned radio

What you will need

IC1	LM386 low-powered amplifier IC
D1	1N34 fixed germanium diode
TD1	Varactor diode MV-2111, 43.1 to 51 pF (Oak Hill Research, Hosfelt Electronics, or Circuit Specialists)
C1	0.001-μF, 50-volt ceramic disc capacitor
C2, C4	220-μF, 25-volt electrolytic capacitor
C3, C6	10-μF, 25-volt electrolytic capacitor
C5	0.05-μF, 50-volt ceramic disc capacitor
C7	0.1-μF, 50-volt ceramic disc capacitor
L1	3 turns of #24 enameled wire wound on toroid coil form
L2	26 turns of #24 enameled wire wound on toroid coil form
R1	10-kilohm, ½-watt fixed resistor
R2	10-kilohm linear control
R3	10-kilohm taper control with SPST switch
R4	10-ohm, ½-watt fixed resistor
J1, J2	Antenna and ground binding posts (Radio Shack, 274-662)
J3	Open-circuit stereo jack (Radio Shack, 274-249)

SW1   Single-pole, single-throw (SPST) switch on rear of R3
B1   9-volt battery
Misc.   Piece of PCB, 8-pin IC dip socket, 9-volt battery
       cable and socket, solder, 4 rubber stick-on feet,
       etc.

You can listen to "Voice of America"; WYFR, Okeechobee, Florida; WRNO, New Orleans, Louisiana; WHRI, South Bend, Indiana; WCSN "Christian News Monitor," Boston, Massachusetts; KUSW, Salt Lake City, Utah; WCCR, Nashville, Tennessee; and BBC relay stations on this radio (Fig. 6-1).

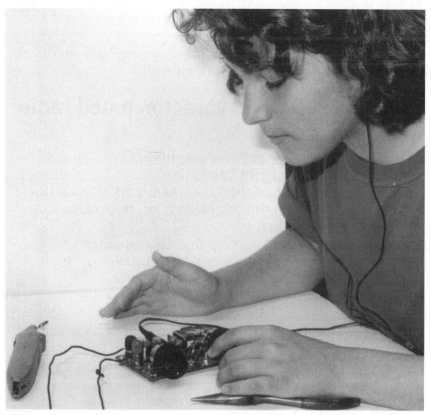

Fig. 6-1 *Tuning in a station with the tuning control of the 15-MHz receiver.*

How the circuit works

You will need a good outside antenna and ground on this radio because no RF amplification is used. The antenna terminal post connects directly to the primary winding of L1 and the ground to

J2. L1 and L2 are wound on a T-50-2 toroid form. In the evening and early morning hours, you can hear stations on 15 MHz at least 2000 miles away. You will need a large tuning knob as these stations are sometimes difficult to separate (Fig. 6-2).

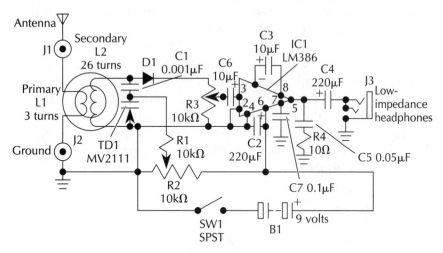

Fig. 6-2 *A simple wiring schematic of the 15-MHz varactor-tuned radio.*

Tuning in L2 is done with a varactor tuning diode (TD1). R2 is the tuning control that varies the dc voltage on the TD1 terminals. C1 isolates the dc voltage from L2 and D1. TD1 has a capacitance from 43.1 to 51 pFs (MV2111). You can replace the varactor diode circuit with a 50-pF variable air capacitor, if desired, however you can keep the cost low by using the varactor diode and R2. Using 12 volts instead of 9 volts increases the tuning.

The 15-MHz tuned-RF signal is detected by diode D1 (1N34). Actually, you might say this little varactor-tuned radio is nothing more than a crystal tuner with IC audio amplification. The weak audio signal is tied to the top side of volume control R3. Believe it or not, on strong signals, you might have to turn down the volume control. The C6 electrolytic capacitor couples the AF signal to pin 3 of IC1.

The low-powered LM386 (IC1) is used as a headphone amplifier. Capacitor C2 should be placed as close to pin 6 as possible to eliminate howling or oscillations. The audio output signal is coupled through C4 to the low-impedance headphone jack. Low-priced, low-impedance headphones are used here in a small stereo jack. Both stereo windings are paralleled by connecting both terminals to the ungrounded jack terminals. SW1 is found on the rear of R3, and turns the negative battery terminal off and on.

Winding the coils

L1 and L2 were wound on a small iron coil toroid form (T-50-2). This round donut is only ½ inch in diameter, so it doesn't take too much wire to wind the coil. Cut off 2 feet of #24 enameled magnet wire. Leave about 1½ inches for terminal connections. The excess can be cut off when the coil is mounted.

Now start winding secondary coil L2. You can start the coil by pushing the excess wire down through the center hole, or pushing it up through the hole. Hold the start of the coil winding with your thumb and forefinger. Grab the end of the excess wire and thread it through the hole. Now pull the rest of the wire through the hole. Be careful here that the wire doesn't kink up. If the wire kinks up, reverse the kinked section and pull the excess wire through (Fig. 6-3).

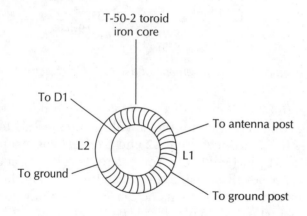

Enlarged view of
1/2" diameter toroid form

Fig. 6-3 *Coil L1 is 3 turns of #24 enameled magnet wire wound over L2, which consists of 26 turns of #24 enameled wire. Both are wound on a T-50-2 toroid iron core form.*

Pull the wire tight each time it is pulled through the hole. Keep the turns of the winding under your thumb. Closely wind a total of 26 turns for L2. If you use #24 enameled wire instead, it does not unravel as long as it is pulled tightly while winding.

Wind on three turns of #24 enameled wire over the center part of L2. The primary winding (L1) can go between the wire turns of L2. Cut off the leads to a length of 1 inch. Scrape all four coil leads and tin with solder. Cut off any coil excess when mounting the coil form on the PC wiring. This coil form goes right over the PC wiring and is located between the four connecting spots.

Building the PC board

The MHz varactor-tuned radio was designed to have all components mounted on one PCB, including the battery and both variable controls. The terminals of both variable resistors are bent over and soldered directly to the PC wiring. Large PC wiring is used for these terminals.

Lay out the PCB as shown in Fig. 6-4. Cut a piece of copper board 5½ × 3 inches. Remember the top of the board has all mounted parts.

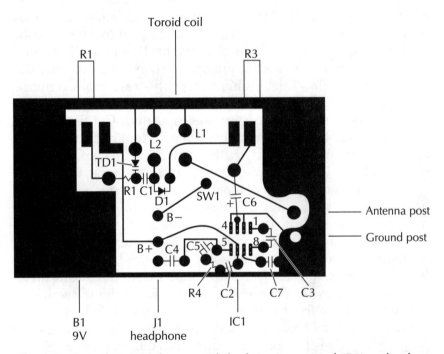

Fig. 6-4 *Complete PCB layout with both tuning control (R2) and volume control (R3) mounted on the wiring side of the PCB.*

The layout of the parts is not critical, except that you need to be sure that the toroid coil connections are as short as possible. Likewise, mount the varactor diode close to the tuned circuits. The small toroid coil is held to the board with the extended coil wires. Overlap the 8 IC1 pins so that when mounted, the socket pins solder on top of the wiring. When the socket pins are flattened out, they extend over the regular IC pin terminals. Make sure all press-on transfers are pressed tightly to the PC copper side.

When etching the board, always look at the board every 15 minutes so you do not over-etch it or destroy the small PC wiring. It should take from 30 to 45 minutes to etch the board. Place a pencil under the etching tray, and tip the tray from side to side to hurry up the process. If you keep the etching solution in a cold area, warming the container of solution under a hot water faucet before using may help the etching process.

Mounting parts

First mount the IC socket. Bend all pins flat. Terminals 1 and 8 can be twisted towards the C8 terminals. Be careful when soldering these terminals. Do not apply too much solder as it may flow into other terminals or wires. But be sure to make a good solder connection. Now check each connection by testing continuity between the top socket pin and its connected wiring. Use the 200-ohm scale of the ohmmeter for this test. Mark terminal one with a felt pen on the PCB.

Next mount all small resistors and capacitors. Cut the terminal leads short, and bend an L in each terminal. The small components are surface mounted directly on the PC wiring. Be sure to observe correct polarity for D1, varactor diode TD1, C2, C3, C4, C6 and C7.

Mount D1 and TD1 with a pair of long-nose pliers to act as a heat sink. Too much heat can destroy either diode. If TD1 gets mounted in backwards, the radio will not work, but it won't destroy the diode when voltage is applied. Simply unsolder it and reverse the two leads. J3 can be soldered to the board with short leads. If the jack moves, place epoxy underneath the plastic area.

Mount IC1 by observing terminal 1. Match the U symbol or dot found on the front end of the IC component. When mounting, you may need to straighten the pins with a pair of long-nose pliers. Make sure all the IC pins are inserted in the socket. Sometimes one or two may slip alongside the socket, rather than in it.

Now mount both variable controls. Bend the control terminal so that the terminals are under the mounted control. Tip the control forward to solder the terminals. Level the control, and on R3 solder the switch lead tightly to the PC wiring to keep the control steady and level. Linear tapered control R2 is mounted in the same manner, with a piece of bare hookup wire at the top that is soldered to the large PC ground wiring. Make sure all controls are level. Of course, you can use a bent metal bracket to hold both controls if desired.

Testing the circuit

Before mounting the 9-volt battery, double check all wiring connections. Make sure IC1 is inserted properly. Check for correct polarity on all components, such as diodes and electrolytic capacitors. It's very easy to solder a small electrolytic capacitor in backwards. Now plug in the battery and pair of headphones. Connect the antenna and ground and try it out (Fig. 6-5).

Fig. 6-5 *A closeup showing how the parts are mounted on the PC board.*

Rotate the volume control fully open. You should hear a little hum. Rotate R2 and tune in the international broadcast stations. You may not hear any stations in the middle of the day. Of course this depends on where you live and how far your radio is from the 15-MHz stations. In the evening, you may have trouble separating the stations.

These stations can be exciting to listen to as they are in British, Spanish and German languages. Several religious stations can be heard, besides the time station WWV. You hear just about any type of broadcast on VOA and BBC. For only a few dollars, this little 15-MHz radio works surprisingly well.

Project 2: Two-band IC radio

What you will need

C1	365-pF capacitor (Antique Electronics Supply, CV-230, or KA7QJY Components 365 pF)
C2, C3, C5	0.1-µF, 50-volt ceramic capacitor
C4	0.22-µF, 50-volt capacitor
L1	12 turns of #24 enameled wire
L2	70 turns of #24 enameled wire
L3	250 turns of #30 enameled wire
Ferrite rod	5 or 7 inch long 0.333 inch diameter (Antique Electronics Supply, PC-185)
J1, J2	Antenna jacks (Radio Shack 274-315)
J3	Stereo headphone jack (Radio Shack, 274-247)
B1	Two AA flashlight batteries
B1 holder	For two AA batteries (Radio Shack 270-382)
SW1	Single-pole, double-throw (SPDT) toggle or rocker type switch
SW2	Single-pole, double-throw (SPDT) miniature toggle switch or push ON-push OFF switch
PC board	2½-×-4½-inch cut from layered PCB
Misc.	Cabinet, knobs, solder, hookup wire, etc.

Three IC semiconductor devices, the ZN414Z, ZN415E and ZN416E, each contain 10-transistor, tuned-radio frequency (TRF) circuits packaged in a TD-92 plastic housing with an 8-pin dip socket. The ZN414Z unit consists of a very high-impedance input stage, several RF amplifier circuits, and a transistor detector, all in one component. The ZN414Z solid-state device must have outside audio amplification.

All components tied to the outside terminals of ZN414Z are included inside the ZN415E and ZN416E, except the tuning capacitor and coil, which are needed in the AM radio (Fig. 6-6). The internal transistor audio circuits are included in the ZN415E package. Besides having an 18 decibel (dB) buffer audio stage, the ZN416E IC also has low-output matching impedance (64 ohms). Only 6 external components are needed to supply a high-gain RF 8-pin IC radio, operating from one flashlight cell, (Fig. 6-7). This little radio drives a pair of low-impedance headphones with plenty of volume.

How the circuit works

Two different AM radio bands can be received by switching different coils into the circuit. The long-wave (lw) band operates below

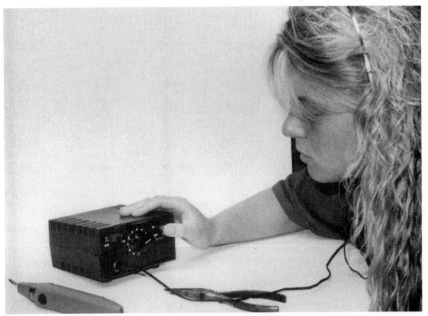

Fig. 6-6 *Simple IC multi-band radio constructed on a PCB using a ZN416E IC component.*

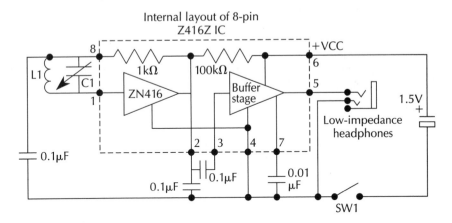

Fig. 6-7 *The ZN414Z semiconductor contains many small components built inside the 8-pin IC core. The ZN416E drives a pair of low-impedance headphones.*

the broadcast band (550 kHz) when a jumbled wound coil is used. The broadcast band coil is wound on the same ferrite rod that medium wave (mw), 550-kHz–1600-kHz frequencies use. SW1 switches in the two different bands at terminal 1 of IC1 (Fig. 6-8).

You will find only four small bypass and coupling capacitors in this circuit. C4 couples the audio from pin 2 to input buffer

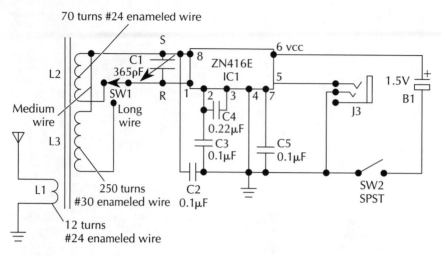

Fig. 6-8 *Only a few components are used with the two-band radio.*

terminal 3. The audio input is found between pin 5 and common ground. The ZN416E IC output feeds into a 64-ohm lead. Instead of grounding the common terminal on the stereo jack (J1), leave the common terminal open, placing the two headphones in series (Fig. 6-9).

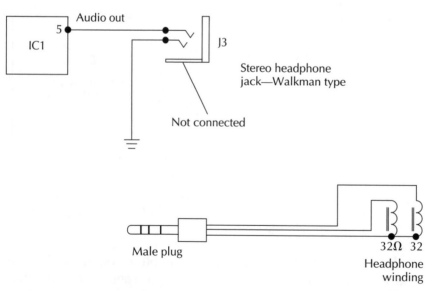

Fig. 6-9 *A regular stereo headphone jack is wired so that the two windings are in series, leaving the common terminal open.*

Winding the coils

Select a five- or seven-inch 0.333-diameter ferrite rod to wind all three coil windings. Wind 250 turns of L3 first since it contains the most turns and is jumble wound. Place L3 in the middle of the ferrite rod. Leave about 6 inches of copper wire from each coil winding for circuit connections. Then wind on 70 turns of #24 enameled wire for L2. Place tape over the ends to prevent the coil from unraveling (Fig. 6-10).

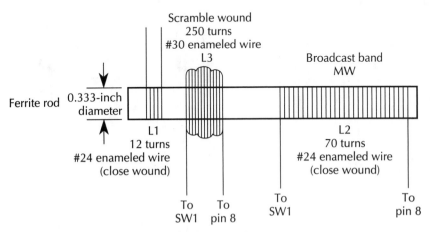

Fig. 6-10 *All three coil windings are wound on one long ferrite form. Two different coils are switched into the circuit, covering the long-wave (lw) and medium-wave (mw) broadcast band.*

Wind 12 turns for L1 using the same wire size, ⅛ inch from L3. The common return of both coils can be soldered together with one hookup wire going to pin 8 of IC1. Solder each coil end to their respective terminals of SW1. Cement the ferrite rod to the back of the case after all the wiring has been completed, and the radio has been tested.

Connecting the batteries

The ZN414E, ZN415E and ZN416E were designed to operate from 1.1 to 1.6 volts dc. In this radio, a dual penlight cell holder was modified to supply 1.5 volts to pin 6. The battery is switched into the ground circuit with SW1.

The two-cell AA battery holder was originally designed to place the cells in series, resulting in a total of 3 volts. Here, the negative spring terminal is soldered with a separate hookup wire. Simply turn one cell around, placing both negative and positive terminals of each cell together. The two cells are now connected in parallel instead of series. A separate lead at the top and bottom connects the battery into the circuit (Fig. 6-11). Of course, one C or D cell can be used instead of AA batteries.

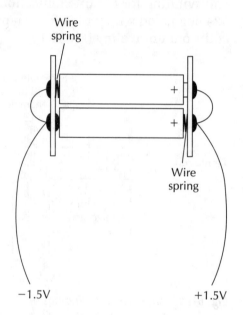

Fig. 6-11 *Only 1.5 volts is needed to power the small radio. Two AA batteries are wired in parallel.*

Laying out the PC board

This radio PCB was designed so that the variable capacitor and the battery mounts on the same board as the radio components. C1 mounts in the middle and B1 to the right. Follow the PC wiring layout shown in Fig. 6-12. Notice all parts are surface mounted on the top side.

Cut a piece of copper PCB 2½ × 4½ inches. Round off each corner with a file or a grinder. Level all saw cuts with a file or a sander. PC wiring was constructed with press-on PC transfers.

When surface mounting the 8-pin IC dip socket, extend the terminals with the same type of press-on IC pin transfers. The socket pins stick out on the PC wiring and may overlap if not extended. These pins are bent flat and can be twisted or aligned for correct PC wiring.

Large copper areas on the board can be made with plastic tape. Radio Shack's PVC electrical tape, ½ inch wide, is ideal. Just overlap each piece of tape to form the large area. Cut and trim the plastic tape with a sharp razor blade. Make sure there

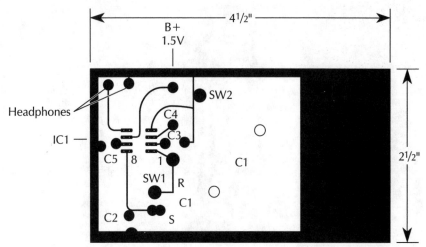

Fig. 6-12 *Cut a 2½-x-4½-inch piece of PCB and etch the board. Both batteries and C1 are mounted on the same PCB.*

are no bubbles under the tape. You can construct the small IC radio on a piece of perfboard, instead of the PCB, if desired.

Drilling holes

Drill two ⁵⁄₃₂-inch holes to mount the variable capacitor (C1). Place the edge of the capacitor to the front edge of the PC board. For bottom mounting, place a piece of paper at the edge of the capacitor, and push mounting holes through the paper with a pencil point. Then lay the paper on the PCB and mark mounting holes. Drill a ⁵⁄₃₂-inch hole in each corner for mounting the PCB in the cabinet.

SW1, SW2 and the headphone jack can be mounted on the front panel. Mount the ferrite coil form at the rear of the radio. Both antenna and ground jacks are mounted on the rear panel.

Mounting parts

Mount and solder all small components before mounting C1 or B1. Line up the 8-pin IC DIP socket over the proper terminals. Be careful not to use too much solder, resulting in pieces of wiring being soldered together. Clean between each IC terminal with a pocketknife blade to remove excess resin or solder. Double check the soldered connections for continuity from the IC pin socket terminal to the PCB wiring. Check between terminals for possible shorts (Fig. 6-13).

Bend a small L in each capacitor lead, and cut it off so that it is short before soldering into position. Check that each connec-

Fig. 6-13 *The small components are placed on top of the PC wiring in a surface-mounted fashion.*

Fig. 6-14 *The completed radio is mounted in a plastic cabinet.*

tion is soldered well and that there are no leads touching one another. Solder the variable capacitor and battery terminals after the small parts have been mounted.

Testing the circuit

Double check all wiring. Make sure no bare wires are touching. Turn on SW2 with a pair of low-impedance headphones plugged in. Set SW1 to the broadcast (mw) band. For local broadcast stations no outside antenna is needed. Rotate C1, and tune in your favorite broadcast station (Fig. 6-14).

Now check the long-wave band (lw). Try late evening or early morning hours for best lw band reception. This IC radio pulls in the local broadcast stations without the outside antenna. L1, J1 and J2 can be eliminated if you want local station reception.

Project 3: IC speaker radio

What you will need

IC1	ZN416E IC RF amplifier/detector (DC Electronics)
IC2	LM386 audio IC
TD1	440-pF varactor diode NTE618 (Hosfelt Electronics or Mouser Electronics)
C1, C6	0.01-µF, 50-volt ceramic capacitor
C2, C3, C4, C5	0.1-µF, 50-volt ceramic capacitor
C7	10-µF, 35-volt electrolytic capacitor
C8, C10	220-µF, 35-volt electrolytic capacitor
C9	0.05-µF, 50-volt ceramic capacitor
C11	2200-µF, 35-volt electrolytic capacitor
L1	45 turns of #24 enameled magnet wire
Ferrite rod	0.333- or ½-inch ferrite rod (Antique Electronic Supply, PC-185)
R1	10-kilohm, ½-watt resistor
R2	10-kilohm linear taper control
R3	1-kilohm control
R4	10-ohm, ½-watt resistor
R5	10-kilohm, ½-watt resistor
SW1	Single-pole, single-throw (SPST) switch on rear of R3
IC sockets	Two 8-pin sockets
PCB	Dual IC board (Radio Shack, 276-159)
Speaker	8-ohm, 3- or 4-inch speaker
Battery holder	Four-C-cell holder (Radio Shack, 270-383)
B1	Four C cells
Misc.	Nuts and bolts, solder, hookup wire, etc.

Only two small IC components are required to provide loud-speaker operation on the broadcast band. IC1 serves as the RF, automotive gain control center (AGC), detector, and amplifier circuits in one small 8-pin DIP socket. Actually, pin 5 of IC1 provides headphone operation. IC1 operates in the 150-kHz to 3-MHz frequency range. In this project, only the broadcast range is used (Fig. 6-15). The only power needed for the speaker radio is four C cells wired in series (+6 V).

Fig. 6-15 *Local AM broadcast stations can be heard over a permanent magnet (PM) speaker.*

How the circuit works

IC1 provides a complete RF amplifier, detector, and AGC circuit and requires only a few capacitors. The ZN416E IC also has a buffered audio output stage. No alignment is necessary with this tuned-radio frequency (TRF) IC circuit. Simple and effective AGC action is obtained with excellent headphone or speaker operation. L1 is tuned with varactor diode TD1 (Fig. 6-16).

The audio is controlled by R3, and coupled to pin 3 of IC2 via C6. The output audio from pin 5 is coupled to the PM speaker through C10. You will have plenty of volume for local AM stations. SW1 turns the 6-volt source off and on with 1.5 volts tapped and fed to pin 6 of IC1.

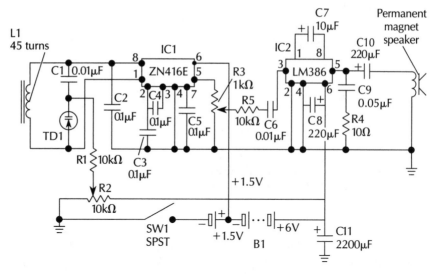

Fig. 6-16 *IC1 contains RF, detector, AGC and one stage of audio circuits, while IC2 drives a 3- or 4-inch speaker.*

Winding the coils

Select a ferrite rod about 5 inches long of ⅓ or ½ inch diameter. Wind on approximately 45 turns of #24 enameled wire. Start about one inch from the end and wind on the total turns. Put a piece of plastic or transparent tape over the starting wire to hold it in place, and wind the wire over the remaining tape. Temporarily place tape over the end winding to hold the coil together. Use coil dope, plastic cement, or clear fingernail polish at the end (Fig. 6-17).

When tuned with the varactor diode (TD1) and variable resistor (R2), the broadcast band should be received. If you can't pick up a local station at 550 or 600 kHz, wind on 5 to 10 more turns. When a station at 550 kHz comes in at the middle rotation of R2 remove turns from the coil. If a broadcast station is heard at approximately 540 and 1400 kHz, you know the complete broadcast band is covered.

Mounting parts

Instead of making an etched PCB, both IC's and small parts are mounted a dual-IC PCB (276-159). Each IC socket is soldered on a separate section, with small components soldered around it. Part layout is not very critical. Just make sure all capacitor leads are short and direct.

L1

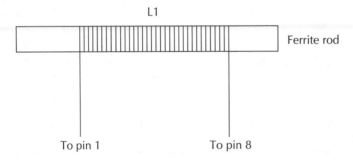

Ferrite rod

To pin 1   To pin 8

Fig. 6-17 *Wind on 45 turns of #24 enameled wire over a*
0.333-inch diameter ferrite rod.

Solder the antenna leads directly on the IC1 PCB. Connect a piece of hookup wire from R1 to R2, with ground and B+ leads. A separate lead is soldered to pin 6 of IC1 for the positive 1.5-volt battery source. Solder hookup wire to pin 5, and attach it to the top of R3. After soldering in the IC sockets to the PCB, run a pocketknife blade between the soldered pins to clean out any resin or extra solder (Fig. 6-18).

Fig. 6-18 *Each IC socket is mounted on a section of the dual IC board.*

Mount all capacitors and resistors around IC2 on the other IC board. Keep all leads short. Mount C8 close to pin 6 of IC2 to prevent oscillations. Solder a piece of hookup wire from pin 6 to the positive terminal on the C cells. The speaker and ground leads are twisted together, and run from C10 to the top of the speaker with the other terminal to ground. Solder a solid bare buss wire (#22) across the extreme top and bottom of the dual IC board for common ground.

Preparing the front panel

Draw an outline of the front panel on a sheet of paper that is about the same size as the front panel. Lay out all the parts that are mounted on the panel. The speaker holes can be large ones with speaker cloth behind it, or small holes without any grill cloth. Place a sheet of perfboard over the speaker outline and mark the small holes with a sharp pencil point. Tape the perfboard to the front panel. These grid holes serve as speaker marking holes. You can use any larger-grid, pre-drilled boards to mark these holes.

Select a small drill bit if you are going to drill out each grid hole. If larger ⅛-inch holes are drilled, skip a hole or two. Just make sure all holes are uniform and provide adequate speaker sound. Also, drill four ⅝-inch holes to mount the 4-inch speakers. Follow Fig. 6-19 for other component mounting holes.

Wiring the circuit

Besides running lead extensions to R2, R3, and the speaker, you will need to connect the two different voltage sources. Solder one side of the switch to common ground and the other to the negative voltage pack. Place a soldering lug between the positive battery terminal after the first cell, and cell #2. Connect the 1.5-volt lead to pin 6 of IC1. Solder a piece of hookup wire at +6 volts on the battery holder to pin 6 of IC2.

Before inserting both IC1 and IC2 into their respective IC sockets, double check all wiring and soldered connections. Verify correct polarity for the capacitors C6, C7, C8, and C10. Locate pin 1 of each IC socket and insert each IC component. Make sure all pins are in the socket.

Rotate SW1 and R3 half way. Try to locate a station with R2. If no stations can be heard, check the polarity of TD1. Unsolder the varactor diode and turn it around. This diode will not be

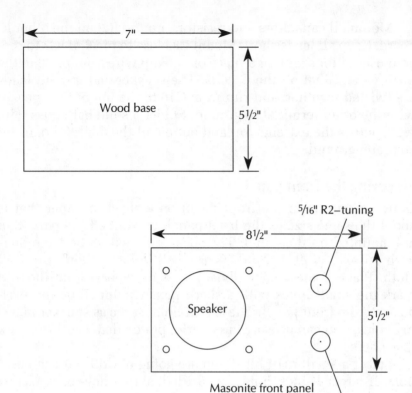

Fig. 6-19 *Drill out the speaker holes in the perfboard using a small drill bit.*

damaged if wired up backwards, but both IC1 and IC2 can be ruined if inserted in the socket the wrong way.

The volume on local broadcast stations should drive the speaker without any problems. In fact, the volume control must be lowered on most local stations. After you are sure your AM receiver is operating, place it in a plastic cabinet.

Building the cabinet

The IC AM radio can be placed in a plastic cabinet large enough to house the small speaker. If placed in a metal cabinet, the antenna rod has to be mounted outside the cabinet. An open-faced wood rear chassis and masonite front was used in our radio project.

Cut a piece of fir or ash wood 5½ × 7 inches for the rear chassis. Saw out a 4½-x-8½-inch piece of masonite for the front panel. After sanding, spray on two coats of clear acrylic or lacquer to protect the surface. Drill out the front panel and place on rub-on transfers for labeling before applying another two coats of spray-on lacquer (Fig. 6-20).

Since tuning diode (TD1) is fairly large in capacitance, only 45 turns is needed on the coil to cover the entire broadcast band. Add or remove a few turns from the coil if stations are not received. To prevent oscillations when the volume is turned fully up, insert R5 (10 kΩ) in series with C6. Also add C11 (2200 µF) to prevent oscillations. C11 can be mounted on the audio board or directly across the +6 volt source.

Fig. 6-20 *Complete the dual-IC AM radio by mounting it into a plastic cabinet.*

Project 4: Throw-away special radio

What you will need

Q1	1S4 vacuum tube, 7 pin
IC1	LM386 audio IC
C1	40–400-pF compression trimmer capacitor (Radio Shack 272-1336, or Antique Electronics Supply CV-421)
C2	200-pF screwdriver variable air capacitor

	(Modified Surplus or KA7QJY Components, 140-pF or 200-pF screwdriver adjustment)
C3	15 pF (KA7QJY Components, Antique Electronics Supply CV-316, or Ocean State Electronics, HF-15)
C4, C7	270-pF silver mica capacitors
C5, C9, C10	10-μF, 35-V electrolytic capacitor
C6, C14	0.1-μF, 35-V ceramic capacitor
C8	0.001-μF, 35-V ceramic capacitor
C11, C12	220-μF, 50-V electrolytic capacitor
C13	0.05-μF, 35-V ceramic capacitor
L1	4 turns of #26 enameled wire
L2	9 turns of #26 enameled wire
L3	18 turns of #26 enameled wire
L4, L5, L6	6 turns of #26 enameled wire
R1	3 megohms
R2	10-kilohm linear taper control
R3	10-kilohm audio taper control (Radio Shack, 271-215)
R4	10-ohm, ½-watt resistor
T1	10-kilohm in 10kΩ primary, 1kΩ secondary interstage transformer (see text)
J1, J2	Antenna and ground posts
J3	Stereo headphone jack (Radio Shack 274-247)
RFC1	2.5-mh choke (KA7QJY Components or Mouser Electronics 434-1250)
Socket	7-pin wafer socket (Antique Electronics Supply, P.S. 201)
SW1	Double-pole, single-throw (DPST) toggle switch
Misc	D cell, dual D-cell battery holder, 9-V snap-on sockets with leads, 8-pin IC DIP socket, etc.
B1-B4	Four 9-V batteries or 1 45-V battery

We've called this radio receiver the throw-away special because it is made from parts that are thrown in the junk box, found on the surplus market, and/or removed from old radios and TV receivers. It operates in a frequency range from 1800 to 8400 kHz.

The coil form came from a piece of plastic drain pipe, and the coil wire was taken out of an old speaker field coil. The variable air capacitor was a surplus adjustable-type that you can purchase to-day for about $1. If you have some old antique junk radios, remove the vernier dial and other knobs for the front panel (Fig. 6-21).

Fig. 6-21   *All of the parts required to build this three-band shortwave re-ceiver come from the junk box, junked radio or TV sets, or from surplus houses.*

T1 was removed from a junked handheld radio, while IC1 was taken from a discarded project. Q1 was taken from a box of old tubes ready to be hauled away. Actually, the wafer-tube socket and headphone jack are the only recently purchased parts.

How the circuit works

The throw-away shortwave receiver operates on the 120-, 80-, or 40-meter band (1800 to 8400 kHz). The antenna feeds into an RF untuned grid circuit at pin 3 of Q1. C2 and C3 make up a tuned-grid circuit (Fig. 6-22). SW2 selects the correct band applied to the tuning capacitor (C2) and bandspread capacitor (C3). C4 and R1 provide grid-leak detection. R1 was made up of three 1-meg-ohm, ½-watt resistors wired in series.

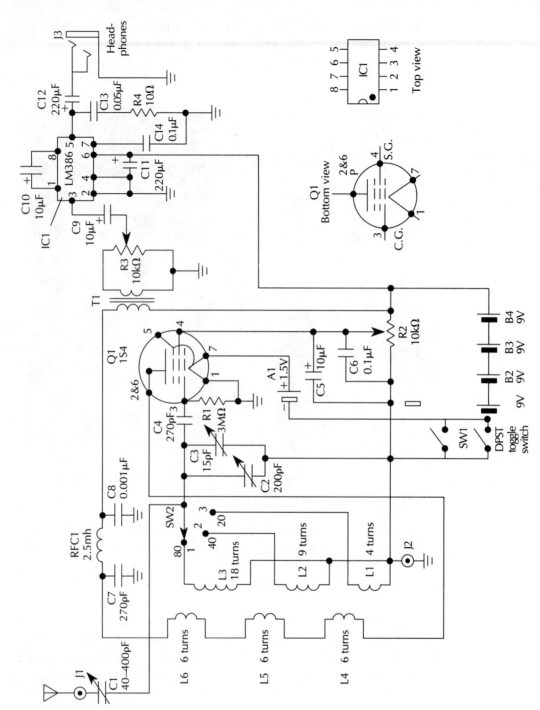

Fig. 6-22 *The wiring diagram of the throw-away special shortwave receiver.*

The regeneration feedback occurs with coils L4, L5, and L6. When SW2 is switched to position one, the entire set of coils (L1, L2, and L3) work on 120 meters. Coils L2 and L1 form the 80-meter band, while only L1 tunes the 40-meter band. If the radio does not oscillate, reverse the coil wire at plate terminal 2 of Q1 (1S4) and the RF choke (RFC 1).

The T1 transformer couples the detected audio signal to IC1. This interstage transformer can be about any impedance and any size. The interstage transformer used here was taken from an old portable radio. The impedance ratio can be 10 to 600, 10 to 5, 20 to 1, or 10 to 2 kilohms. In fact, a telephone coupling transformer will work okay.

Because high-impedance headphones are hard to get, as well as quite expensive, the LM386 IC amplifier was used. The IC socket had a broken off lug but was repaired with a piece of wire extension. IC1 was swiped from another discarded audio project. The rest of the amplifier parts were taken from the junk box and from other projects laying around.

Winding the coils

The six coils are wound on a piece of PVC pipe leftover after the plumber installed a new sink. Cut the coil form 2½ inches long. The plastic PVC pipe is 1½ inches in diameter. Drill two $\frac{5}{32}$-inch holes in each end for mounting the coil form to the wood chassis.

Lay out the different coil windings with small holes $\frac{3}{16}$-inch apart. Each coil end wire can be threaded through these holes to prevent them from unwinding. Just bend the excess wire (about 3 inches) over the end of the coil form to keep it taut and out of the way (Fig. 6-23).

Start with L6 and leave about 6 inches of extra wire to connect to the tube circuit. Wind on 6 turns of #26 enameled wire. Actually, the wire was taken from an old speaker field coil assembly. But you can purchase #26 enameled wire, or take it from small dc motors, field coil assemblies on anything else that may have used it.

Space L3 $\frac{3}{16}$ inch away from the end of L6, and wind on a total of 18 turns of the same size wire. Secure the end through the next hole. If you have a drill press, you can drill each hole as you finish winding each coil. Draw a pencil line down the center of the PVC pipe so all holes will be drilled in line. Pull the excess wire of L3 over the edge of the coil to keep it from unwinding. Remember, all coils are close wound.

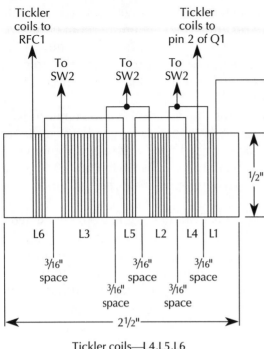

Fig. 6-23 *Coil information for all coils. The three-band coils each have a separate tickler coil.*

Tickler coils—L4,L5,L6
Grid coils—L1,L2,L3

L4,L5,L6—6 turns of #26 enameled wire
L1—4 turns of #26 enameled wire
L2—9 turns of #26 enameled wire
L3—18 turns of #26 enameled wire

Wind all coils in the same manner. Keep each coil about ³⁄₁₆ inch away from the other. When you are done with the last winding, apply coil dope or model cement over each coil winding. Let the cement set for a couple of hours. You should have six separate coils when finished.

Connecting the coils

After the cement is dry, cut each coil end, leaving a small amount of excess wire to overlap, except for the coil windings at each end. Leave these ends long so they can be soldered into the coil circuits. Loop the wires, clean the enamel off the wires with a pocketknife, and tin the ends with solder. Solder all tickler turns together. Now solder all main coil windings together. Leave a loop so flexible hookup wire can be soldered at the taps. Connect hookup wire from the coil to the respective coil switch assembly (SW2).

Now you should have all tickler coil windings (L4, L5 and L6) looped and soldered together. Check coil continuity with the low-ohm range of the ohmmeter. All three main tuning coils (L1, L2 and L3) are also looped and soldered together. Check these, too, with a continuity test. Leave the end of L4 and L6 extra long to tie into tickler coil circuits.

Connect each coil wire to its respective place on the terminals of SW2. This switch is a 2-pole, 6-position switch, but only one section with three different positions is used. SW2 was a surplus component.

Solder the end of L4 to pin 2 of the tube socket. The other end of L6 solders to the choke coil circuit. If the regenerative circuit does not oscillate, reverse the two wire leads at the tube socket and RFC1.

Remodeling the tuning capacitor

Pick up a piece of thin copper 5/16-inch tubing to fit over the screwdriver hub of the variable capacitor. Cut a length of tubing 1½ inches long. The tubing should fit snug over the adjustable nut adjustment. Cut a piece of ¼-inch control shaft off the old 2-inch volume control. If the shaft is loose inside the tubing, wrap plastic tape over the shaft so it will fit snug (Fig. 6-24).

Fig. 6-24 *The variable air capacitor came from a surplus market for about $1. A piece of brass tubing, a control shaft, tape, and epoxy converted the capacitor into a regular tuning capacitor.*

Slip the brass tubing over the screw nut on the variable capacitor. Mix up epoxy and place it inside the brass tubing. Also place epoxy over the tape on the control shaft. Insert the shaft against the screwdriver adjustment of the variable capacitor through the tubing. Apply epoxy around the brass tubing and the control shaft. The control shaft should be straight. Let the epoxy set overnight. Now you have saved a few bucks and have a variable capacitor with an extended shaft! Small brass tubing and wood dowel material can be picked up at hobby and hardware stores.

Preparing the perfboard chassis

Cut a 2½-×-3-inch piece of scrap perfboard for the tube and IC chassis. Mount the wafer-tube socket at one end. Drill a number of small holes in a circle for the tube socket. Perfect the circle with a round rat-tail file. Drill four ⁹⁄₆₄-inch bit holes in each corner for perfboard mounting (Fig. 6-25).

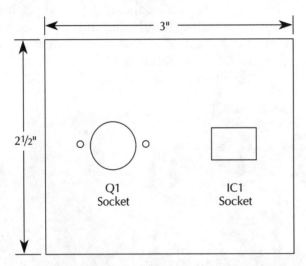

Fig. 6-25 *The perfboard chassis was cut from a 2½-×-3-inch spare piece.*

Mount the tube socket with small bolts and nuts to the perfboard. Place the IC socket opposite the tube socket and bend over the tabs. Connect all components to the tube socket, except the coil and variable capacitor. Mount and solder all small components into the circuit. Cement the small interstage transformer after the wiring connections are made to the perfboard. Solder all extending wires to the different controls before mounting the tube. Small-size solder works best on IC pin terminals.

Building the cabinet

The front panel and rear chassis are made of scrap masonite and pine board. In fact, the front panel was cut from a piece of masonite display board. Cut the front panel 5½ × 9½ inches and the rear chassis piece 6 × 9 inches.

Lay out the front panel as shown in Fig. 6-26. All panel control and switch holes were made with a ⁵⁄₁₆-inch bit. Drill a ¼-inch hole for the stereo headphone jack. Drill a ⁷⁄₁₆-inch hole for the vernier dial assembly. Two small ⅛-inch holes were drilled at the top to hold mounting bolts.

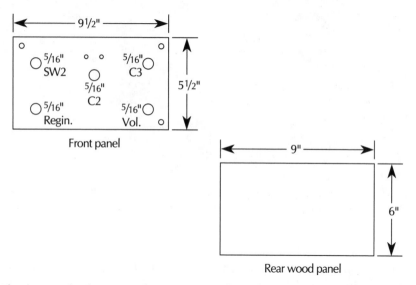

Fig. 6-26 *The front panel was cut from a piece of masonite display board, and the rear chassis was cut from a piece of scrap pine board.*

After all holes are drilled in the front panel, spray on two coats of auto black enamel paint. If dial transfers are to be added, spray on two coats of clear lacquer over the letters. Here, the four dial assemblies were cut from slick cardboard, lettered and numbered, then a piece of clear laminated plastic sheet was placed over each dial assembly. Cut the plastic sheet about ¼ inch larger than the cardboard dials to hold them against the front panel.

Connecting the circuit

After the tube socket and IC components are soldered on the chassis, connect all leads from the perfboard chassis to the proper outside components. Connect the tickler coil and main coil from the coil form to the chassis. Cut the coil wires as short as possible (Fig. 6-27).

Fig. 6-27 *Connecting the wires to the various components and soldering them into the circuit.*

Solder an extension of shielded cable to the volume control from the small interstage transformer. Connect another shielded cable from the volume control to pin 3 of the IC socket. Extend leads from the regeneration control to B+, and to the ground connection. SW1 should be a double-pole, single-throw (DPST) switch so both A and B batteries will turn OFF at the same time.

Connect extension leads to the ON/OFF switch and terminal 7 of Q1 for the filament connections. Solder the four 9-volt batteries in series to the B+ (36 V) and switch terminal. Make sure both the A and B battery minus supplies are tied to one side of SW1 (Fig. 6-28). Twist two flexible leads to connect from the chassis to the stereo headphone jack. A 45-volt battery will work fine for the B power supply, if one is handy.

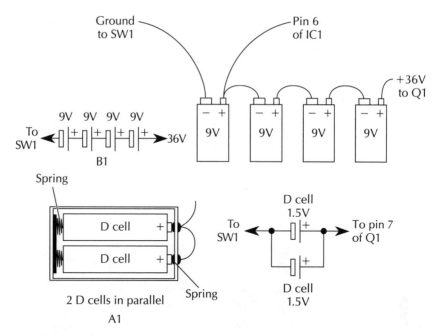

Fig. 6-28 *Connect the two 1.5-volt D cells in parallel. The four B or 9-volt batteries were connected in series for a total of +36 volts.*

Testing the circuit

Double check all components and chassis wiring. Make sure battery terminals are correct. Check the polarity of all the electrolytic capacitors. Connect and insert both A and B batteries. Plug in the headphone. Check for pin 1 of IC1, and insert it into the socket. Plug in the small battery tube. Connect the antenna and ground.

Rotate the regeneration control half way. Turn on the volume control and the switch. You should hear noise with the band switch at position number 1 (80 M). Fully mesh C3 and start rotating C2 (Fig. 6-29 on page 220). Remember, shortwave stations come in best at night, or early in the morning. Check all three bands. You will be surprised at how many shortwave stations you can tune in on this throw-away SW receiver. Rotate the bandspread capacitor (C3) to spread out the stations so they can easily be tuned in.

Project 5: Solar cell radio

What you will need

L1	95 turns of #24 or #26 enameled wire on 0.5 or 0.333-inch diameter ferrite rod.
C1	365-pF variable capacitor (KA7QJY

	Components or Antique Electronic Supply)
C2, C3, C4, C5	0.1-µF, 50-V ceramic capacitor
C6	220-µF, 15-volt electrolytic capacitor
IC1	ZN416E (DC Electronics)
J1	Plastic stereo headphone jack
Solar cells	Four pieces of ¼- or 2½-inch solar cell, four 25 mA or larger, 1.5- or 2-volts total
PC board	5-×-7-inch single-sided PCB
Misc.	8-pin IC socket, solder, bolts and nuts, 6 plastic feet, etc.

Fig. 6-29 *Back view of the completed receiver, ready to be tuned in to the shortwave stations.*

The solar cell radio is a little radio you can build that will last forever. You don't need to worry about replacing batteries, for none are required. This radio is powered by the sun or an overhead lamp. No volume control or ON/OFF switch is found in this radio. The radio can operate all the time if placed near the light (Fig. 6-30).

All components, including solar cells, are mounted on one 5-×-7-inch PCB. All parts are mounted on top of the PCB. This solar cell radio operates with one IC components (ZN416E). IC1 combines the equivalent of 10 RF transistors in one 8-pin case (Fig. 6-31). The tuned-radio frequency (TRF) circuit includes RF, detector, and buffer stages.

Fig. 6-30   *The solar cell radio operates from four solar pieces (1.5 V) and will run for years.*

The buffer stage drives a pair of stereo headphones wired in series for a load of 16 to 32 ohms. The volume is excellent with low-impedance headphones. Just leave the ground terminal of the jack open.

How the circuit works

Only a few electronic parts are found in this solar powered radio. The ferrite antenna coil picks up the stations, and they are tuned in with C1. Pins 1 and 8 are the input terminals of IC1. Ceramic bypass capacitors are found in the ground circuit (Fig. 6-32).

The audio output is fed from pin 5 to the headphone jack. Solar power is applied at terminal 6 and ground. Because this radio is powered by the solar cells, you don't have to worry about replacing batteries, and you don't need an ON/OFF switch or vol-

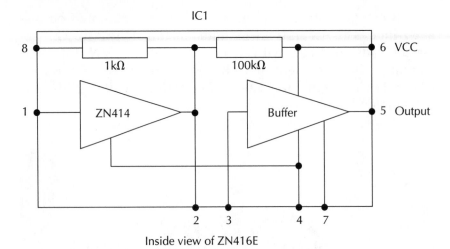

Fig. 6-31   *The inside components of the ZN416E IC consist of an RF, detector, and audio amp circuits built inside the IC core.*

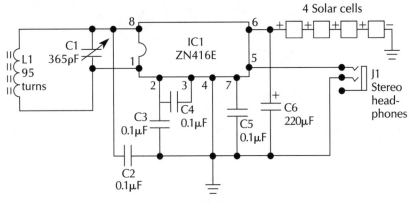

Fig. 6-32   *The solar cell radio circuit is very simple with only nine outside
components.*

ume control. The four solar cells furnish power to operate the
broadcast circuit. IC1 plugs into an 8-pin DIP socket. Actually,
IC1 pulls less than 5 mA of current.

Winding the coils

Select a 0.5- or 0.333-inch-diameter ferrite rod to wind the antenna coil (L1). Place a piece of tape at one end, at the start of the
wire. This holds the winding in position. Now wind on about 95
turns of #24 or 26 enameled wire. Wind each turn close to the

next one. Do not overlap any turns. Keep the wire taut while winding the coil (Fig. 6-33).

Place a piece of tape over the end of the coil to prevent the wire from unraveling. C1 and L1 should tune the entire broadcast band (530 to 1600 kHz). If a station at 540 kHz cannot be tuned in with C1 fully meshed, wind on a couple more turns of wire. When a lower frequency station comes in the middle of the band, remove turns until stations can be heard at the lower and higher ends of the band. Secure the coil wire with tape after any wire adjustments have been made. Leave long leads on the coil until the coil assembly is mounted, then cut to the required length.

Fig. 6-33 *Wind on 95 turns of #24 enameled wire over a 0.333-ferrite rod. Turn the PCB to bring in distant stations or to lower the volume on local broadcast stations.*

Laying out the PCB

Select a single-sided PCB about 5 × 7 inches to mount all the parts, including the solar cells, on. Bend all 8 pins on the IC socket so it will lay flat on the PCB. Place IC connection symbols on the PCB (Fig. 6-34). Draw a rough pencil sketch around the pin terminals and lay the IC connections over it. The IC socket is mounted directly behind the stereo headphone jack (J1).

Place four solar cell pieces evenly spaced on the top edge of

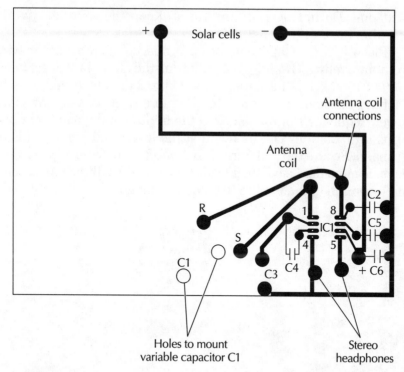

Fig. 6-34 *All components are mounted on one 5-x-7-inch PCB.*

the board. Place the solar pieces together to make a complete circle. Each cell is connected in series, and then joined at the center of the circle. Remember, all parts are mounted on the top of the PCB. Lay out the PC wiring in the right hand corner.

A larger glass dish or pan is needed to etch this large PCB. The etching process will take a little longer than usual, since a greater area needs to be etched away. Recheck the whole board for faulty wiring after the etching process is complete.

Constructing the solar cell

Cut four pieces of fine bare hookup wire about 2 inches long for connecting the solar cells. Solder each lead to the bottom of each cell. The bottom silver side is the positive terminal (+). Make the soldered connection as flat as possible so the cell will lay fairly flat. Do not leave any sharp points of solder. Solder each wire so it will connect on top to the next cell.

Bend the wire end up on the outside of the cell where it will solder to the top of the next cell. These wires can be cut to length after each cell is mounted. Cement each solar cell to the PCB with rubber silicone cement.

Remember, each cell is wired in series with the next solar cell. The positive side (bottom) must connect to the negative side (top) of the next cell. The top side of the solar cells are always negative. Leave the two flat ends of the connecting cells to be soldered to the positive and negative pads.

After all cells are cemented into position and the cement dries, connect the cells in series. Start at the positive terminal of the number 1 cell (Fig. 6-35). Solder the bottom (positive) terminal to pin 6 of IC1. Cut the bottom wire of cell 2 and solder it to the top of cell 1. Notice the top (negative) side of each solar cell has small veins and one larger one where each top wire is connected.

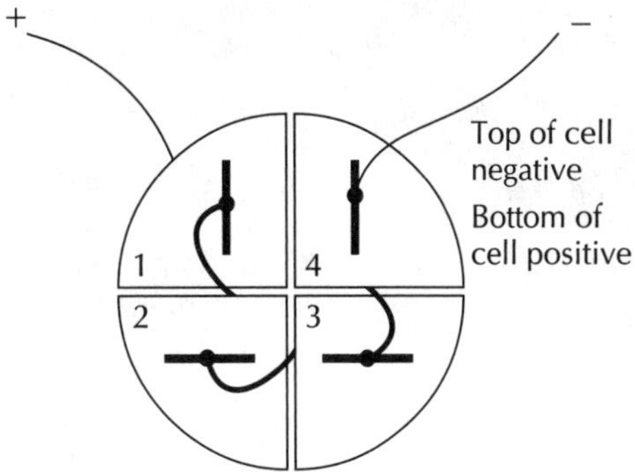

Fig. 6-35 *A closeup of the solar cells wired in series. Be very careful when soldering the top wire.*

Top of cell negative

Bottom of cell positive

Continue soldering as described until all solar cells are wired in series. The top terminal of cell 4 goes to ground (Fig. 6-36).

Be careful not to apply excessive pressure on the cells or they will crack. Also, be careful not to bend each connecting wire or the cells will break in two. Carefully solder the wire on the center line. Cut the wire to length and hold it down with a screwdriver or knife blade while soldering.

Check the total voltage when all the cells are wired with the 2-volt dc range of the voltmeter. Measure voltage at the positive and negative circles. Place a 100-watt lamp over the cells. If the voltage is below 0.75 volts dc, a poorly soldered connection or broken cell exists (Fig. 6-37). Now check the total voltage across each cell to find the bad connection. Under bright sunlight, the voltage should be from 1.4 to 2 volts.

Mounting parts

After the holes are drilled for the variable capacitor, mount all the solar cells. Remember to connect the cells in series. Connect each set of four with the last top to be soldered to the circle. Cement each cell flat against the etched board. Form the four dif-

Fig. 6-36 *Notice all the cells are wired in series. They are cemented with rubber silicone cement to the top of the PCB.*

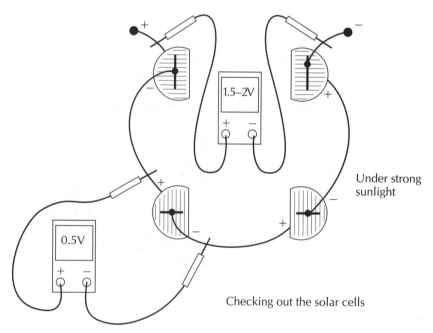

Under strong sunlight

Checking out the solar cells

Fig. 6-37 *Each cell should measure 0.5 volts under sunlight. The total voltage should be between 1.4 and 2 volts dc.*

ferent cells in a large circle. Make sure each bottom cell lead is at the top before cementing it into position. Cement each cell with a thin layer of rubber silicone cement. Let the cement dry before soldering the cells into the circuit.

Next, mount the small IC socket. Make sure each pin is over the right piece of wiring. Mount all small bypass capacitors with bent leads. Form a small L-shaped lead at the bottom of each capacitor. Solder each lead into the circuit. Mount the large variable capacitor with two short bolts from underneath the chassis.

Place the ferrite antenna rod on the plastic supports, and cement it into position (Fig. 6-38). Solder the two antenna leads to the respective circles. Mount the stereo headphone jacks and tie to the chassis with bare hookup wire. Double check all wiring of the solar cells, antenna, phone jack, and variable capacitor.

Fig. 6-38 *A closeup view of how the antenna rod and solar cells are mounted.*

Testing the circuit

To test, plug in the headphone and place the radio under a 100-watt lamp. If the sun is out, try it outdoors. You should hear several local broadcast stations as you tune across the broadcast band. In fact, two stations were heard on my own solar cell radio 100 miles away.

Finish up the radio project by placing six rubber feet on the bottom of the chassis. Place two in the middle so the PCB will not warp. Now you can hear music until the lights go out.

❖7
Special radio projects

FOUR EXCITING RADIO PROJECTS TO BUILD ARE IN THIS CHAPTER: building a band locater, adding single sideband (SSB) and continuous wave (CW) to your existing shortwave receiver, using a camcorder battery to operate a radio, and building an antique shortwave (SW) radio. These projects are very simple, and a couple of them can even be constructed in one evening.

With the crystal-operated band locater circuit, you can add up to 12 different crystals for band location. Only five bands were used in this project, but they cover the 160, 80, 60, 40, and 19-meter bands.

Most of the ham radio operators listen to single sideband (SSB) or continuous wave (CW) stations. Unless you have a beat-frequency oscillator (BFO) in your shortwave receiver, voices sound garbled. You can build this BFO circuit and listen to the different ham bands on a shortwave receiver using a 455 kHz intermediate frequency (IF).

You need an ac power supply or batteries to operate your electronic or radio projects. Unless the batteries you are using are the rechargeable type, you can use up several batteries within a few hours of radio operation. One project in this chapter shows you how you can build a camcorder battery source that provides 5, 6, 9, and 12 volts, and can be recharged simply by slipping it into the camcorder charger.

The last project in this chapter is an antique regenerative shortwave radio, just like Grandpa built in the late 1920s and early 1930s. Two tubes form the regenerative and audio circuits, which use a dc power supply. The filament voltage for the two 2.8-volt tubes operate from two 1.5 volt batteries in series. B+ voltage for both screen and plate voltages comes from four 9-volt batteries wired in series.

Although these four projects are not new or innovative, they are educational, useful, and provide lots of fun.

Project 1: Band locator project

What you will need

Q1	FET transistor MPF 102
LED1	Blinking LED (Radio Shack, 276-036)
C1	100-pF silver mica capacitor
C2	180-pF silver mica capacitor
R1	100-kilohm, ½-watt resistor
RFC1	2.5-mh choke coil-10 μH to 2.5 mh will do (KA7QJY Components)
SW1	5-position rotary switch (Radio Shack, 275-1385)
SW2	Push on-push off switch (Radio Shack, 275-011)
B1	9-volt battery
Battery holder	To hold 9-volt battery (DC Electronics, 1291)
Crystals	purchased at Digi-Key Corporation, Hosfelt Electronics, Inc., All Electronics, Circuit Specialists, or DC Electronics
Box	4¾ × 2½ × 1⅟₁₆ inches (Radio Shack, 270-222)
Misc.	Bolts & nuts, solder, hookup wire, etc.

When winding your own coils and using various tuning capacitors, sometimes it is difficult to know what band of frequencies the shortwave radio is operating in. You can use another shortwave receiver to locate a certain station and compare that signal with your own shortwave receiver. Of course, this takes a lot of time. The shortwave frequencies can also be located with a frequency counter instrument, except that they are quite expensive. The most efficient and inexpensive way to locate frequencies is by building this simple band locator circuit. The circuit works by switching in several different crystals. In fact, you can add up to 12 crystals with the 12-position switch (SW1). By selecting several low-priced crystals, most shortwave bands can be received (Fig. 7-1).

Today, the low-priced crystal costs anywhere from less than $1 up to $2.50. House unit (HU) or house case (HC)-18 crystals can be purchased from most mail-order firms. A complete line of quartz crystals can be purchased from Digi-Key Corporation. Hosfelt Electronics also has a variety of HC-18 crystals for less than $1 each.

How the circuit works

The crystal oscillator circuit operates around the field-effect transistor (FET). Each crystal is switched into the circuit using SW1. Keep all the leads from the PCB to the switch as short as

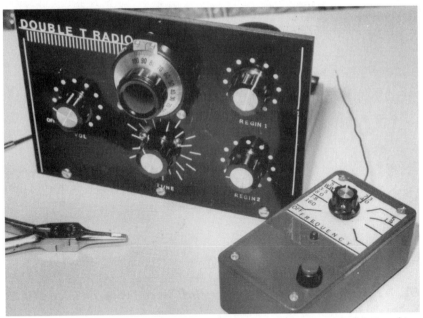

Fig. 7-1 *Know what frequency your radio is operating on with this Band Locator circuit.*

possible. The crystal oscillator circuit is powered with a 9-volt battery through light-emitting diode 1 (LED 1) (Fig. 7-2).

LED 1 is a pulsating or blinking LED device and is wired in series with the battery circuit. The LED provides a pulsating or intermittent dc applied to the drain terminal (D) of Q1. Besides a clicking noise, you will hear an intermittent, beeping signal which is easily recognized, especially in the CW and ham bands. When the receiver is tuned to beeping signal, you have located the correct frequency.

You can switch in as many crystals as required, although in this project we used only five. See Table 7-1 for the crystals required for the various bands.

	Crystal (MHz)	Band covered (meter)
	1.8432	160
	2.000	120
	3.57954	80
Table 7-1	5.000	60 (WWV)
	7.3728	40
	14.31818	20
	15.000	19

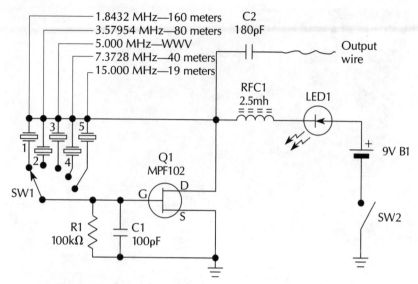

Fig. 7-2 *The simple crystal oscillator circuit with five or more crystals for changing frequency bands.*

Laying out the PC board

Cut off a 2-x-4½-inch piece of PC board from a single-sided board. Lay out the PC wiring as shown in Fig. 7-3. Two inches of the board is left with copper finish where the 9-volt battery is mounted. Etching time is about 40 minutes. Double check the PC wiring for breaks. If necessary, check with an ohmmeter.

Drill a ³⁄₁₆-inch hole in the center of the board to mount against the plastic box. Place a metal 9-volt battery holder on the board, and drill out two holes for mounting. The 9-volt battery can easily be snapped into position as it is mounted on the PC board.

Mounting parts

First mount the metal battery holder. Bolt it into position. Connect insulated wires from the correct battery terminals to the PC wiring. Next mount all small resistors and capacitors. Use a pair of long-nose pliers as a heat sink while soldering the Q1 terminals. The small crystals are soldered last.

Go over the PCB and make sure Q1 and LED 1 have correct polarity. If LED 1 is in backwards, no voltage is applied to Q1. Recheck the terminal leads of Q1. C1 and C2 can be silver mica capacitors.

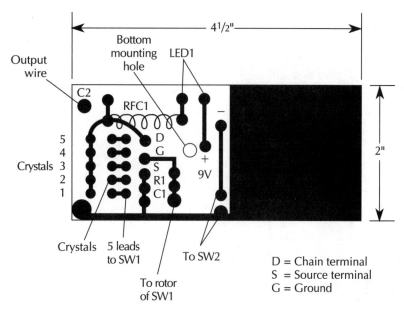

Fig. 7-3 *The PCB layout, cut from a larger single-sided PCB.*

Building the chassis

This small oscillator can be mounted in a metal or plastic box. You might not need the outside lead if it is mounted inside a plastic box. The crystal oscillator radiates a loud signal that can be picked up when the unit is placed alongside the shortwave receiver. If the radio is built in a metal case, loosely wrap the outside lead around the antenna input lead.

In the example, the oscillator was placed in a 3/4- ×-2½- ×-1⅛-inch plastic box. SW1, LED 1, and SW2 were mounted on the top panel. Drill a ⅜-inch hole for SW1, 7/16-inch hole for the LED, and 3/16-inch hole for SW2 (Fig. 7-4).

Testing the circuit

Before mounting the PCB and parts into the plastic box, try out the circuit. Insert the 9-V battery and turn on SW2. Tune in the shortwave receiver to the 60-meter band (WWV-time station) and rotate SW1 to 5.000 MHz. You should hear a beeping sound when the correct frequency is tuned in. The LED will blink ON and OFF while operating.

If the unit is too close to the shortwave receiver, it can blank out the sound. Try different positions, with the crystal oscillator

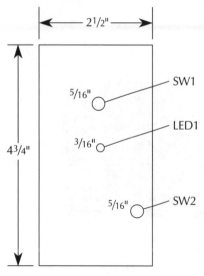

SW1

5/16"

LED1

3/16"

Fig. 7-4 *Front plastic panel with layout of the holes.*

4³/4"

5/16"

SW2

Front panel layout

near the antenna or the RF coil. The shortwave commercial re-ceiver will pick up the different signals when the unit is placed alongside (Fig. 7-5).

Fig. 7-5 *Just position the crystal oscillator alongside a shortwave receiver to locate the various shortwave ham bands.*

If the LED does not blink, check the battery, SW2, and LED 1. Reverse the leads on the LED when 9 volts is measured at one terminal, but it does not operate. Check Q1 with a transistor tester or diode tester if the FET is suspected. This is a simple oscillator circuit and should operate easily.

Marking the front panel

Mark the front panel using switch decals or rub-on symbols and numbers. Mark the frequency on the dial with the associated meter band. Cement the dial to the front panel with model or plastic cement. Cut a larger piece of laminated plastic, ¼-inch wider than the panel to cover the frequency band decal.

The band select circuit lets you know at a glance the operating frequency of your homemade shortwave receiver.

Project 2: CW and SSB adaptor project

What you will need

Q1	MPF102 FET
T1	455-kHz IF transformer (small yellow identification dot on top)
C1	10-pF or 15-pF variable tuning capacitor
C2, C4	180-pF silver mica capacitor
C3	220-µF, 35-volt electrolytic capacitor
R1	1 kilohm ¼ watt resistor
SW1	Single pole, single throw (SPST) switch
B1	9-volt battery (Eliminate B1 if SW1 is tapped into receiver power source.)
Misc.	Perfboard, battery clip, bracket, solder, hookup wires, etc.

To bring out continuous wave (CW) and single sideband (SSB) signals in your superhet shortwave receiver, build this CW/SSB adaptor. The 455-kHz oscillator, or beat-frequency oscillator, replaces the missing carrier in SSB operation. Also, this adaptor converts CW transmissions into audible signal (Fig. 7-6).

In the early days of radio, the ham bands could easily be heard just by tuning them in. But today there are so many bands, SSB offers a greater opportunity for more amateurs to operate on the designated bands. When tuning in the SSB without a BFO, the ham operator sounds garbled.

Fig. 7-6 *The single sideband (SSB) crystal adaptor is mounted on a small perfboard chassis.*

This shortwave adaptor can be connected to any shortwave receiver that is without sideband reception, or with a shortwave converter. Of course, it only performs with a receiver having a 455-kHz intermediate frequency (IF). With the adaptor, the bands listed in Table 7-2 can be heard.

Table 7-2

Ham radio SSB frequencies (kHz)

3,800–4,000
7,150–7,300
14,200–14,350
21,250–21,450
28,500–29,700

Morse code CW signals (kHz)

3,500–3,800
7,000–7,150
14,000–14,200
21,000–21,250
28,000–28,500

How the circuit works

The BFO circuit consists of an FET (MP102) and the tapped secondary coil of T1 (Fig. 7-7). T1 is a small 455-kHz IF transformer

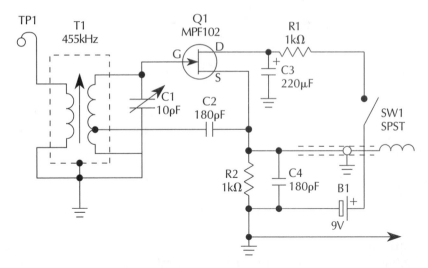

Fig. 7-7 *The 455-kHz oscillator circuit using a field effect transistor (FET) for Q1. The output signal is taken from the source circuit of Q1.*

with a primary and secondary winding. Feedback occurs between the T1 tapped coil and C2 to the source terminal (S) of Q1. Variable tuning capacitor C1 provides BFO tuning. The tunable frequency can be checked at the primary test point (TP1).

When C1 is rotated, it tunes to both the lower and high frequency side of the intermediate frequency. By tuning the BFO circuit, you can separate the garbled voice, and make it clean and audible. The variable, iron-core adjustment of T1 can be tuned to either higher or lower SSB frequencies.

The output of the beat-frequency oscillator is taken from the source terminal (S). Connect a flexible, insulated hookup wire to the shortwave receiver. The insulated wire can be twisted around the AM diode detector or IF stage in the shortwave receiver. Do not directly solder the BFO wire to the IF circuit. For CW and SSB operation, couple the input signal to the 455-kHz transformer. Tune in the garbled ham radio signal, and flip on the BFO switch (SW1). Rotate C1 until the voice is clear and clean. Each whistle you hear is a ham station.

Building the chassis

To build the chassis, first cut a piece of perfboard 1¼- ×-1½-inches for the main chassis (Fig. 7-8). Square all sides on the sander or with a flat file. All parts are mounted on the perfboard except the 9-volt battery, or the operating supply voltage.

Make an angle bracket out of a scrap piece of metal or alum-

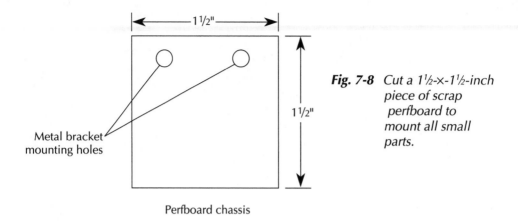

Fig. 7-8 Cut a 1½-x-1½-inch piece of scrap perfboard to mount all small parts.

Perfboard chassis

inum for the variable tuning capacitor. Cut the metal 1¼ × 1½ inches, and bend a ¼-inch lip for mounting. Drill a ¼-inch hole for the small capacitor (C1). Drill two small ⁹⁄₆₄-bit holes to hold the bracket to the perfboard.

Drill the small holes to mount the tabs of the 455-kHz transformer. Mount T1 at the rear of the chassis. Bend over the small tabs to hold the transformer in position until it is wired. Next mount the metal bracket and C1. Mount and solder the small components into the circuit. Place a bare bus wire around the outside bottom area of the perfboard for all ground connections.

Solder the transformer outside terminal and tab to the ground wire. Loop the bus wire near these outside connections. Loop the ground part connections through the perfboard and over the bus ground wire. Keep all leads as short as possible.

The SSB adaptor can be operated from a 9-volt battery or connected to the shortwave receiver voltage circuits.

Connect a small, insulated solid hookup wire to the primary winding of test point 1 (TP1). You can check the IF tunable frequency with a frequency meter connected to TP1 or to the output wire. The frequency meter will show whether or not the BFO circuit is oscillating. When soldering Q1 into the circuit, use a pair of long-nose pliers as a heat sink. Place a shielded-cable wire over the extension lead so it will not radiate to other circuits.

Testing the circuit

The BFO signal can be heard with the broadcast radio tuned to lower frequencies. Place the SSB adaptor near the radio and rotate the tuning capacitor. Listen for a variable tone signal. Align T1 with the frequency meter or 455-kHz signal generator.

Wrap the insulated signal wire around the IF detector or IF circuit. Tune in a ham station on the shortwave converter or receiver. Flip on SW1 and tune R2 until the audio is clear. Sometimes you may have to rotate C1 several times before you get clear audio.

Project 3: Using a camcorder battery as a power source

What you will need

IC1	9-volt, 1-amp regulator (7809)
IC2	6-volt, 1-amp regulator (7806)
IC3	5-volt, 1-amp regulator (7805)
C1	3300-μF, 35-volt electrolytic capacitor
C2,C3	
C4,C5	0.1-μF, 50-volt ceramic capacitor
J1,J4	Red banana jack
J2, J3, J5	Black banana jacks
PCB	Two 4½-×-8-inch pieces of double-sided PCB, cut from a larger piece
Cabinet plastic box	7¾ × 4⅜ × 2⅜ inches (Radio Shack, 270-232)
Misc.	Bolts and nuts, spring-type brass or copper for the slip-on contacts, solder, etc.

Why not use the camcorder battery in your camcorder as a dc voltage source to power your radio projects? These batteries have long operating ampere-hours, and can be used again and again since they are rechargeable (Fig. 7-9). If the battery becomes weak, just charge it up again with the camcorder battery charger.

Without damaging the battery contacts, you can build a slide-lock arrangement on your radio board, like those found on the battery charger. Simply slide the battery into the holder, and tap different voltage sources from several voltage jacks. The battery holder must be a solid, heavy-duty type with connect and disconnect features.

The 12-volt battery used in this project operates a VHS camcorder. Just about any camcorder battery will do. Simply build a lock arrangement to hold the battery in position. Different voltage sources can be tapped with 1-ampere (amp) voltage regulators.

Fig. 7-9 *The camcorder battery adaptor can be used to power the small radio projects in this book.*

How the circuit works

The dc voltage source connects to the battery slide terminals. The various voltage sources are 12, 9, 6, and 5 volts. Fixed voltage regulators are used for the 9, 6, and 5-volt sources (IC1, IC2, and IC3). C1 provides filtering for all voltage sources (Fig. 7-10). C2, C3, C4, C5 capacitors provide RF filtering if there is feedback from the radio on each voltage source.

Building the slide-lock adaptor

The slide-lock adaptor is made from a double-sided PCB, and is mounted on a large plastic box. The plastic box measures 7¾ × 4⅜ × 2⅝ inches. Remove the metal cover (you can use it in another project). Build the slide-lock adaptor to fit in the top of the plastic box. Draw the top outline of the plastic box (Fig. 7-11).

Cut a piece of double-sided copper PCB to fit over the large box opening. This PCB holds the battery connections on one side, the surface-mounted components on the bottom side, and it serves as a support for the slotted holder. Round off the corners to fit inside the plastic box. Use a hacksaw or a saber saw with a metal blade to speed up the cutting process.

Next cut out another piece of copper board with the slotted guides (Fig. 7-12). If you use another camcorder battery, simply follow the slotted area on the battery, charger, or camcorder. The slotted areas can be cut out with a large flat or three-corner file. These slotted areas should be very accurate so the battery will load and unload easily. The slotted board has one end open and

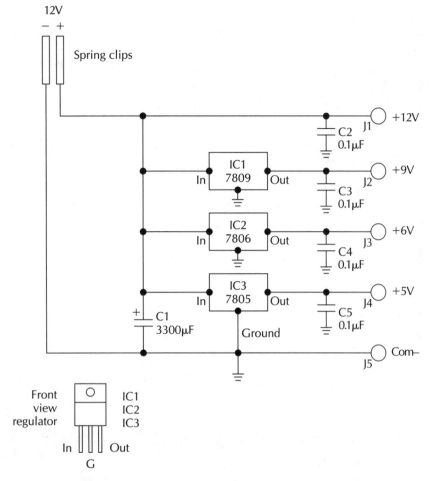

Fig. 7-10 *This circuit uses three different voltage regulators.*

the other end solid. The open end is for loading the battery. Make sure the lip of each slotted area is square and fits the grooves of the battery exactly.

Cut ⅝-inch strips for shims, from the copper board that was cut from the center of the slotted piece. Place a piece on each side and one at the top or end. These shims provide space for the battery flanges to ride in. Make sure shims do not protrude into the slotted area. Cement these pieces to the slotted board with epoxy or rubber silicone cement. The shims must be placed between the slotted board and the cover.

After the cement sets, drill ¹¹⁄₆₄-inch holes towards the outside edge, so the bolts won't prevent the battery from loading and unloading. All three pieces should be drilled at the same time so

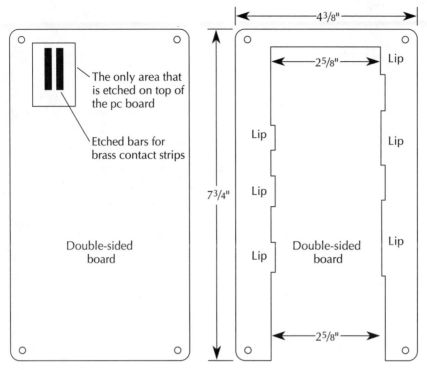

Fig. 7-11   *The slide-lock adapter is made from double-sided PCB material.*

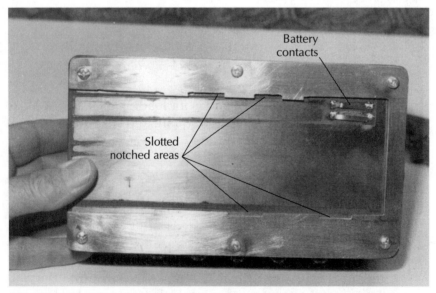

Fig. 7-12   *The slotted guides for the 12-V camcorder battery are the same on the camcorder or on the battery charger.*

the holes will line up correctly. Bolt the top piece (with the shims) to the top cover. Of course, the top cover must be etched, the parts mounted, and wires connected for the various voltage jacks before the boards are bolted together.

Laying out the PC board

The voltage regulators are wired on the bottom of the double- sided board. The outside area is left solid for added support. Only the inside voltage regulator circuit is etched away. Follow the PC wiring layout in Fig. 7-13 so the parts can be soldered in a surface-mounted arrangement. The top side of the copper board is left solid, except where the battery slide clips are mounted (Fig. 7-14).

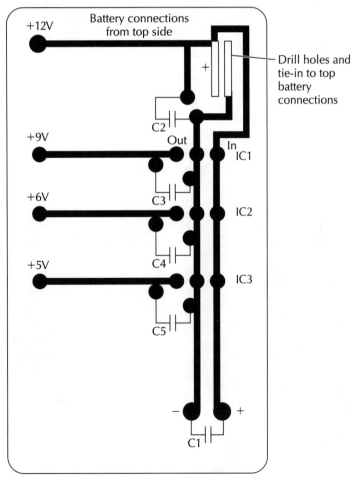

Fig. 7-13 *The PC wiring is on the bottom side of the PCB, with parts mounted on the surface.*

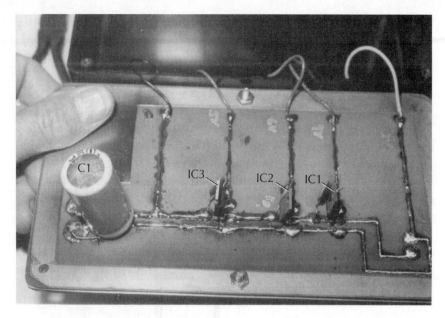

Fig. 7-14 *All parts are mounted on the PCB except the voltage jacks.*

Since a large area of the board will not be etched, use PVC rubber tape over the area. Place the tape side-by-side to protect the copper area. Cut around the edges with a razor blade so the ends will not unravel. A larger etching tray is needed to etch both sides of the double-sided copper board.

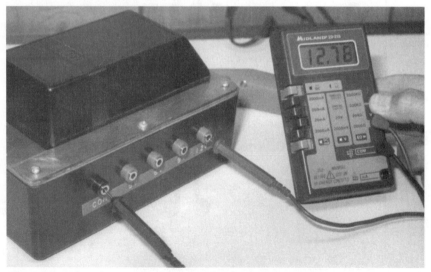

Fig. 7-15 *After the parts are mounted, take a voltage measurement on each voltage jack using a digital multimeter (DMM).*

Testing the circuit

After the slotted area is bolted to the etched board, solder the flexible hookup wire to the respective voltage jacks. Insert the camcorder battery and check each voltage source with the DMM (Fig. 7-15). Bolt the entire slide-lock assembly in the regular screw holes of the plastic box. Now you do not have to worry about using those alkaline batteries. Remove the camcorder battery when not in use.

Project 4: Antique shortwave set

What you will need

Q1, Q2	3S4 vacuum tubes (Antique Electronic Supply)
C1	6-50-pF trimmer capacitor (Radio Shack, 272-1340)
C2	100-pF variable capacitor (KA7QJY Components)
C3	15-pF variable capacitor (KA7QJY Components)
C4, C5	270-pF silver mica capacitor
C6	0.2-μF, 50-volt ceramic capacitor (can be two 0.1-μF capacitors in parallel)
C7, C8	0.01-μF, 50-volt ceramic capacitor
L1	56 turns of #24 enameled wire
L2	15 turns of #24 enameled wire
R1	2.2-megohm resistor
R2	50-kilohm linear taper control (Mouser Electronics #316-1000
R3	47-kilohm, ½-watt resistor
R4	500-kilohm audio taper control
R5	1-megohm, ½-watt resistor
RFC1	2.5-mh choke coil, 3 layer
SW1	Double-pole, single-throw (DPST) switch
Tube sockets	7-pin wafer sockets (Antique Electronics Supply, P.S.-201)
Front panel	6-x-8-inch phenolic panel cut from an 8-x-12-inch piece (Antique Electronics Supply)
J1, J2, J3 & J4	Two-position post jacks (Radio Shack, 274-315 or equivalent)
Headphones	2000-ohm high impedance

| B1 | Two 1.5-volt D-cell batteries wired in series |
| B2 | Four 9-volt batteries wired in series |

In the 1920s and 1930s, the regenerative circuit became famous for the shortwave receiver (Fig. 7-16). Of course, tubes were used with high-impedance headphones. The regenerative radio had a tickler feedback coil, and the point of oscillation was found with the regeneration control. Coils L1 and L2 were wound on plastic coil forms.

Fig. 7-16 *Your completed antique shortwave receiver looks like the one Grandpa built in the 1930's.*

How the circuit works

C1 couples the shortwave signal picked up by the antenna to coil L1. C1 should be wide open for initial operation. Grid leak-capacitor detection is provided by R1 and C4. R1 may be made up of a couple of resistors for the total 2.2 megohms (Fig. 7-17). The feedback circuit consists of L2, from pin 2 of Q1, to the RF choke coil (RFC1). Regeneration is controlled with R2, which varies the voltage on the screen grid terminal of Q1.

Notice that both Q1 and Q2 are actually audio output tubes.

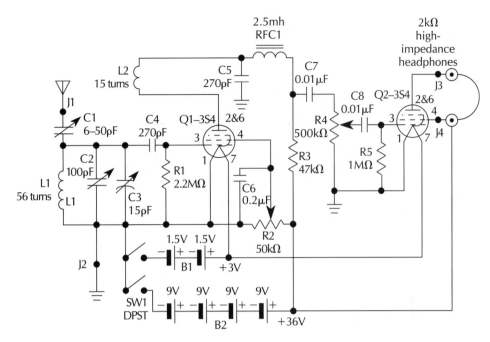

Fig. 7-17 *The regenerative circuit consists of two 3S4 tubes working from batteries.*

Q1 is used in the circuit as the regenerative detector tube. The audio signal is taken from the choke coil (C7) and coupled to the volume control (R4). Q2 is another 3S4 tube used as an output amplifier. Actually, two 1S4 tubes can be used in place of the 3S4, as they are identical except for the filament voltage. The 1S4 tubes use only 1.5 volts for the filaments on pins 1 and 7.

Winding the coils

Cut off 2½ inches from a plastic 1½-inch-diameter drain or PVC pipe. Drill a hole ¼ inch from the end. Wind on 15 turns of #24 enameled wire for the tickler coil (L2). At the end of L2, drill ⅟₁₆-inch hole to insert the wire and prevent it from unraveling. Space L ⅛-inch away from L2 by drilling another ⅟₁₆-inch hole (Fig. 7-18).

Start L1 and wind on 56 turns of #24 enameled wire for a length of 1⅜ inches for an 80-meter coil. Space the windings over the 1⅜ inches. Wind the coil closely until 45 turns are on the core. Drill a ⅟₁₆-inch hole at the 1⅜-inch mark, and insert the end of L1. Then space each turn with the knife blade so it will fill up the en-

80 Meter Band L1, 56 turns Tickler coil, 15 turns 3500–4000 kHz, SSB 3800–4000 kHz
40 Meter Band L1, 18 turns L2, 5 turns 7000–7300 kHz, SSB 7150–7300 kHz
20 Meter Band L1, 10 turns L2, tickler coil, 5 turns 14,000–14,350 kHz, SSB 14,200–14,350 kHz

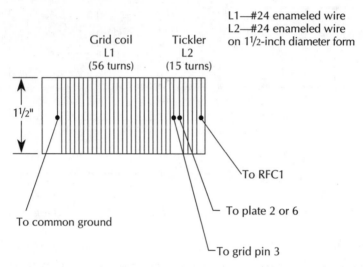

Fig. 7-18 *L1 consists of 56 turns of #24 enameled wire, while the tickler coil L2 has 15 turns for 80 meter band.*

tire required length. It's best to drill two ¹⁄₁₆-inch holes at the start and end of each winding so the wire will not unwind. Feed the coil end in and out of the second hole.

Drill two ⁵⁄₃₂-inch holes in each end for mounting. These holes will be at the opposite ends from the coil winding start and finish. Place plastic cement or coil dope over the windings to hold the spacing in position. If the coil is to be mounted vertically, place two mounting holes on board end.

Making the front panel

Cut a 6- ×-8-inch piece of phenolic panel from a larger piece. This ³⁄₁₆-inch-thick black panel can be obtained from Antique Electronic Supply (see Chapter 9 for details). Lay out the required holes as shown in Fig. 7-19. Protect the front panel with a piece of paper showing hole layouts placed over the front area while drilling the holes. Tape the paper ends to the back of the panel. This prevents accidental scratching or marring of the front panel.

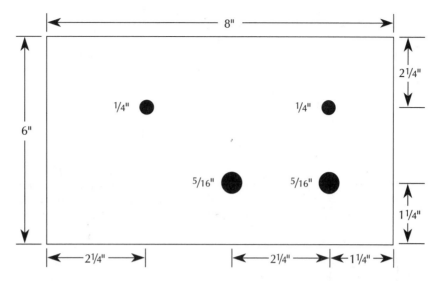

Fig. 7-19 *The front panel is layed out on a black phenolic panel.*

After drilling all front panel holes, place rub-on letter transfers on the panel for the dial assemblies. Wash off the panel with soap and water to remove any finger smudges. A dry transfer marking set can be purchased from most electronic mail order firms. Spray on a couple coats of clear lacquer or hobby spray.

Building the perfboard chassis

Cut a 2½ × 4 inch piece of perfboard from a larger piece (Fig. 7-20). Drill out the holes for the wafer tube sockets. This ¾-inch hole can be made with a large drill bit, or small holes can be drilled inside the tube socket circle. Drill a ⁵⁄₃₂-inch hole in each corner to mount the perfboard chassis to the wooden chassis.

Drill ⁵⁄₃₂-inch holes to mount the antenna, ground, and headphone posts. Make sure the antenna post is toward pin 3 of the tube socket. The headphone posts can be mounted near the audio output tube (Q2). Mount the Q1 socket towards the antenna coil and variable capacitors to prevent long RF leads. After all parts are mounted and wired up, place one inch plastic spacers between the perfboard chassis and the wood chassis.

Mounting the variable capacitors

Both variable capacitors (C2 and C3) are mounted on a separate piece of masonite or fiber board to prevent stray capacitance.

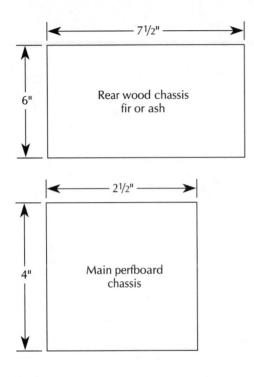

Fig. 7-20 *The main tube chassis is 2 ½ × 4 inches, and is cut from a piece of perfboard and mounted on the rear of a wooden chassis.*

Move the board back 2 inches from the front panel (Fig. 7-21). Because of this, the variable capacitor shafts must be connected to plastic shaft material pushed through the front panel. The shafts can be coupled together with shaft couplers or a large, heavy-duty spring.

Two inexpensive methods of shaft coupling can be used. Select a spring just a little smaller than the ¼-inch shaft and push over the capacitor metal and plastic shaft. Another method is to use shrink tubing that is a little larger than ¼ inch, and slip it over both ends of the shafts. Apply heat with an electric hair dryer. Place epoxy cement at both ends and inside the tubing. The second method is to use plastic tubing and metal nipple fittings.

Make sure the ¼-inch plastic shaft sticks through the ¼-inch front panel hole, at least ⅝ inch. The ¼-inch mounting holes of both front and back panels must be directly in line. First drill out the front panel holes. Screw the front panel to the main wood base. Then place the second panel up against the back of the front panel, and mark the two ¼-inch shaft holes. Cement tin foil to the back of the front panel.

The second panel is held in position with a metal strip at the bottom. This metal strip can be cut from a piece of aluminum or sheet metal. Drill three bolt holes to hold it to the second panel.

Fig. 7-21 *Both variable capacitors are mounted on another masonite panel mounted about two inches back from the front panel to help eliminate stray capacitance.*

Three wood screws hold the panel in position in the main wood chassis.

Assembling the unit

Mount the power supply chassis between the two panels. The rear panel is braced to the front panel for added support. Cement tin foil to the back of the front panel for hand capacity before mounting (Fig. 7-22).

Solder shielded cable from the volume control to the corresponding grid circuits. Use #22 solid hookup wire between the components. Don't forget to ground the center terminal of both tube sockets.

Tape one side of the ac cord to the transformer and the other side to the switch terminal. Place rubber silicone cement over the switch terminals to prevent shock. Lace the cables together with the cord.

Making the shaft extensions

You will find that variable capacitor shaft extensions are difficult to obtain through mail order. The ones that are available are quite expensive. If you cannot pick them up at a local electronic

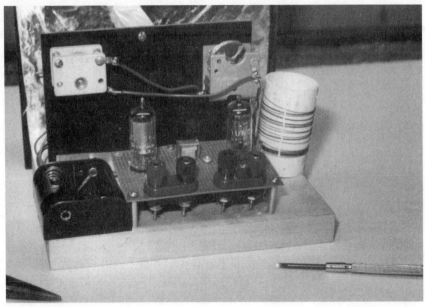

Fig. 7-22 *A rear view of the wooden chassis. Notice how the different components are mounted.*

store, make your own extensions. In fact, you can make several for under $2 out of plastic tubing (Fig. 7-23).

You can make shaft couplings from hollow rods or plastic tubing. Insulated plastic tubing with a ⅜-inch outside diameter and slightly less than ¼-inch inside diameter can be picked up at a local hardware store. A polyurethane toilet hookup tube fits snugly over the variable capacitor or control shaft.

You may need to use a little force to push the shaft out. Measure the desired length, and cut it with a hacksaw blade or pocketknife. The 15-inch, ⅜-inch-diameter toilet hookup tube was picked up at a hardware store. Place epoxy or plastic cement at the end of the extension if it starts to slip.

A 6-inch-long, galvanized ⅜-inch-diameter metal nipple will make at least 3 or 4 small shaft extensions. The inside diameter is exactly ¼ inch, and fits snugly over the variable capacitor shaft. Metal-tapped bolts hold the two components together.

After cutting the shaft extension to the correct length, drill out two ⁶⁄₃₂-inch bolts at each end. Drill a ⁷⁄₆₄-inch bit hole, ¼ inch from each end. Tap out the hole with a ⁶⁄₃₂-inch tap. A small tap wrench and ⁶⁄₃₂-inch tap threads shape the holes for the required small bolts. Place two ¼-inch long, ⁶⁄₃₂-inch bolts at each end. Since the ⅜-inch nipple cost only about $1, you now have sev-

Fig. 7-23 *You can make low-priced shaft extensions out of heavy plastic tubing and metal nipples found at the local hardware store.*

eral cheap shaft entensions. These parts can be picked up at your local hardware store.

Using low-impedance headphones

You can use a set of low-impedance headphones with the SW receiver instead of a pair of high-impedance, high-cost head phones. Clip a 2000 or 2500-ohm primary winding with an 8-ohm secondary at the headphone terminal posts. The higher impedance primary winding results in greater volume. Then connect a pair of low-impedance headphones to the secondary side.

Hook up the IC amp as shown in Chapter 2, for more audio output. Simply insert a 4700-ohm, ½-watt resistor to headphone jacks J3 and J4. Clip the input terminals of the IC amp to the resistor. Now your antique receiver has plenty of volume with a cheap pair of stereo headphones.

For greater volume, add an interstage transformer connected in place of R3 with the secondary winding soldered to volume control R4. Choose a driver transformer with a 1:3 ratio im-pedance. For example, a primary winding impedance of 10k and a secondary winding impedance of 2k center tapped will work. Leave the center tap connection of the interstage transformer open.

❖❖8
Using the TDA7000 IC chip in radios

THE SIGNETICS TDA7000 SINGLE-CHIP FM RECEIVER CHIP IS USED to build three different receivers in this chapter. A direct-conversion, 20–30-meter shortwave receiver combines the mixer, oscillator, and one IF section of the TDA7000. The varactor-tuner receiver uses toroid coils and tuning diodes. Last, but not least, is a three-band superhet receiver project using a ceramic filter and an IF stage.

The TDA7000 FM receiver chip is an 18-pin IC with mixer, local oscillator, and two IF and detector stages. Although the chip was designed for FM reception, it is used in these receiver projects for the AM band. The chip can be purchased from DC Electronics at a low cost of about $6 (Fig. 8-1).

Fig. 8-1 *The TDA7000 18-pin IC chip is used in a direct-conversion, toroid coil, and superhet receiver in this chapter.*

In the direct-conversion shortwave receiver, only the mixer, oscillator, and one IF stage is used as an audio preamplifier. A VFO circuit is tuned with a 50-pF variable capacitor. The coils are wound by hand. The direct-conversion SW receiver is simple to build, and receives SSB and CW signals (Fig. 8-2).

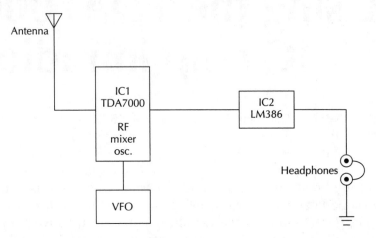

Fig. 8-2 *Block diagram of a direct-conversion receiver using the TDA7000 chip.*

The second receiver project uses the same circuits, but it receives a different set of frequencies, and uses different toroid coils. These coils are tuned with varactor diodes. A vernier-dial assembly separates the many shortwave stations (Fig. 8-3).

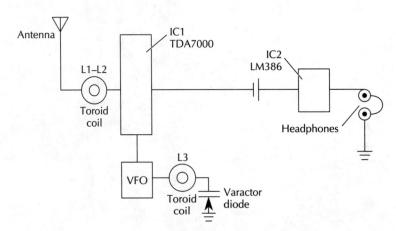

Fig. 8-3 *Block diagram of the toroid coil, varactor-tuned shortwave receiver using the TDA7000 IC.*

The last TDA7000 receiver project is a superhet, three-band shortwave receiver. Ceramic IF and shielded IF stages are used with separate diodes to tune in SSB and CW. The CW and SSB beat frequency oscillator (BFO) is built on a separate PCB. This superhet can be operated using headphones or a 4-inch speaker (Fig. 8-4). Let's begin with receiver number one. We can build all three receivers since they are fairly cheap and easy to put together.

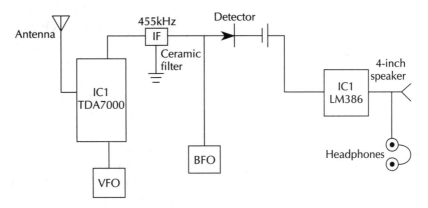

Fig. 8-4   *Block diagram of a superhet receiver using the TDA7000 IC.*

Project 1:
Direct-conversion shortwave receiver

What you will need

IC1	Signetics TDA7000 18 pin chip (DC Electronics, TDA7000, $5.95)
IC2	LM386 audio IC
C1, C6	50-pF variable miniature capacitor (Antique Electronics Supply, CV-325, or KA7QJY Components, 50-pF, or Ocean State Electronics, HF-50)
C2, C4, C7, C8, and C14	0.1-µF, 50-volt ceramic capacitor
C3	0.001-µF, 50-volt ceramic capacitor
C5	0.002-µF, 50-volt ceramic capacitor
C9	10-µF, 35-volt electrolytic radial capacitor

C10, C11, C13	220-μF, 35-volt electrolytic radial capacitor
C12	0.05-μF, 50-volt ceramic capacitor
R1	10-kilohm audio taper control with SPST switch
R2	100-ohm, ½-watt fixed resistor
R3	10-ohm, ½-watt fixed resistor
T1	38 turns, #30 enameled wire on L43-6 shielded coil form (Amidon Associates, Inc. or Ocean State Electronics coil forms, L45-7-PCT-B-4)
T2	38 turns, #30 enameled wire on coil form as above (tapped coil)
J1	Antenna input jack (Radio Shack, 274-346)
J2	Stereo headphone jack (Radio Shack, 274-247)
SW1	Single-pole, single-throw (SPST) switch on back of R1
SW2	Single-pole, double-throw (SPDT) toggle switch
Reduction gear	For C6 (Jackson Bros. of England 6:1 ball drive with ¼ input and ¼ output, or KA7QJY Components, #4511, or Oak Hill Research, #BD01)

Note: A vernier dial assembly with an 8:1 ratio drive can be used here with knob instead of above if you do not want to make front dial assembly (Ocean State Electronics VD112-10 or Oak Hills Research #BD02)

Cabinet	Metal utility 6 × 9 × 5 (Hosfelt Electronics, Inc. #14-124 or equivalent)
PCB	2¼ x 5 inches, double-sided PCB

The direct conversion receiver works on the 20–40-meter band with single sideband (SSB) and CW reception (Fig. 8-5). Only the oscillator and mixer sections are used for the direct-conversion process. The variable-frequency oscillator (VFO) coil

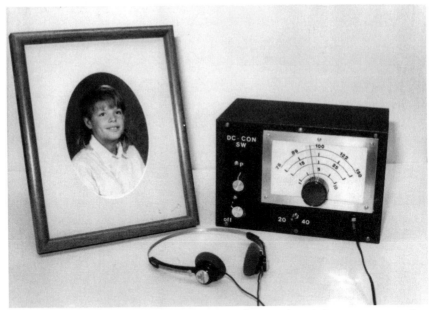

Fig. 8-5   *The tunable VFO coil (T2) provides two-band shortwave reception on the 20- and 40-meter band.*

(T2) provides two-band reception with a tapped oscillator coil. The two bands cover from 6-kHz to 14.475-kHz frequencies.

How the circuit works

The input coil (T1) operates as a balanced RF coil attached to terminals 13 and 14 of IC1. C1 peaks up the incoming signal with L2. The 18-pin TDA700 IC provides mixer, oscillator, and IF (used as audio) stages, feeding the detected signal output to IC2. T2 operates in a VFO circuit on pin 6 of IC1 (Fig. 8-6).

The 20- and 40-meter bands are switched in the circuit with SW2, and tuned with a 50-pF variable capacitor (C6). Because T1 is a broadband circuit, the oscillator circuit is changed to cover both bands with SW2. T2 and T1 coils are wound on commercial adjustable-slug coil forms.

Internally, the audio is taken from pin 9 of IC1 with a stage of amplification. The audio is coupled from IC1 to the volume control (R1) through C8. R1 controls the volume applied to input terminal 3 of IC2. IC2 drives a pair of low-impedance headphones or a speaker. The audio output at pin 5 is coupled to J2 with C11.

SW1 supplies 12-Vdc power to the shortwave receiver. The 12-volt source may operate from a 12-V camcorder battery or

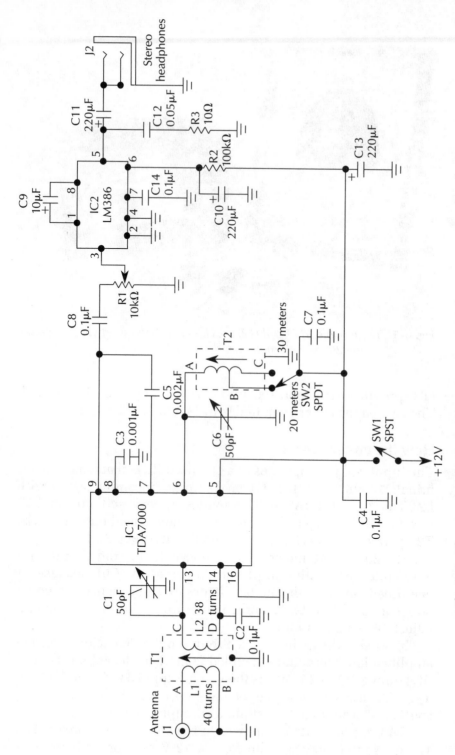

Fig. 8-6 *The circuit uses IC1 as an RF (with VFO), mixer, and oscillator circuit.*

eight flashlight cells. C10, C13 and R2 provide decoupling and a dc filter network.

Shielded cable is used from the antenna input jack (J1) to the primary of T1. Shielded cable is needed on the lead from R1 to pin 3 of IC2.

All leads must be kept as short as possible and shielded cable must be used from SW2. The copper PCB is mounted away from the front panel since a 6:1 reduction gear assembly is needed for tuning C6 (Fig. 8-7). A homemade dial assembly (instructions are given later in this chapter) is attached to the metal front cover. Mount the small receiver in a metal cabinet to prevent broadcast and high-powered shortwave station interference.

Reduction gear assembly

Fig. 8-7 *Mount the double-sided PCB away from the front panel with a 6:1 reduction gear assembly.*

Winding the coils

Select two shielded coil forms from Amidon Associates, Inc. (L43-6), or from Ocean State Electronics (L45-7-PCT-B-4) to wind T1 and T2 on. Remove the shield and start winding the coil (L2) over the plastic form (Fig. 8-8).

Clean off the end of the wire with a knife blade and wrap a couple of turns on the outside terminal that has three coil terminals. Start with the matching terminal (C) at pin 13 of IC1. Wind on 16 turns of #30 enameled wire, close wound. Place a piece of transparent tape over the winding. Cut tape ¼-inch wide and

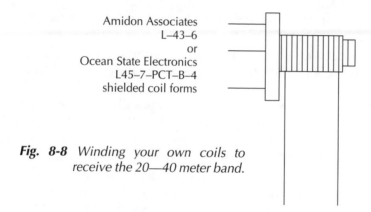

Amidon Associates
L–43–6
or
Ocean State Electronics
L45–7–PCT–B–4
shielded coil forms

Fig. 8-8 *Winding your own coils to receive the 20—40 meter band.*

long enough to just cover the winding. Then wind on another 16 turns towards the coil terminals. Add another strip of tape. Finish the final 8 turns of L2, making a total of 38 turns. Place a strip of tape over the coil. Scrape and wind the coil end around the other outside terminal (Fig. 8-9).

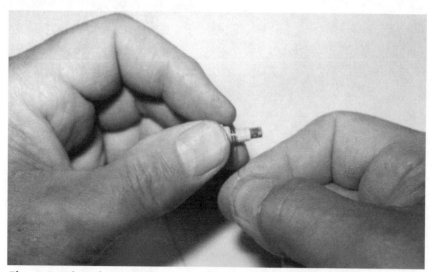

Fig. 8-9 *The plastic coil is wound with #30 enameled wire, wound in layers.*

Start the primary winding (A-B on L1) on two opposite terminals of the coil. Wind on a total of 10 turns of #30 enameled wire. Make sure the tape does not extend beyond the top of the coil. Bend the small coil terminals back into their original position. Solder all 4 terminal leads. Be careful not to apply too much heat as it can loosen up the coil terminals. Replace the shield.

Check each coil's continuity between the separate windings and from the shield to the coil terminals with an ohmmeter.

Start with the bottom coil lug (A) of the VFO coil (T2) and wrap wire around the terminal. Wind on 16 turns of #30 enameled wire. Place a piece of tape on the turns. Then continue to wind another 8 turns of the coil towards the coil terminals. Clean off the top wire area, and loop it around the center coil terminal (B). Do not cut the coil wire. Add on another ¼-inch piece of tape. Continue to wind another 14 turns on the coil (C). Use tape to hold it in position.

The total number of turns for T1 should be 38 turns tapped at the 24th turn from the top (A) of the coil. The 24 turns are for the 20-meter band, and the 38 turns are for the 30–40-meter band. SW2 switches in the 20- or 40-meter band. Band A to C covers 6 kHz to 9.5 kHz, while band A to B covers 9.25 kHz to 14,475 kHz.

All coil windings are close wound. A layer of winding takes up 16 turns of #30 enameled wire. Try not to overlap each turn over the previous wire. Continue to wind all coils in the same direction. The tapped coil wire can be wrapped around the center coil terminal (B), and then you can keep on winding to the end terminal (C).

Check the continuity of each coil before and after they are mounted. If the ohmmeter shows the coil is open, double check the soldered terminal and coil connections. Check the coil terminals to see if they are grounded against the outside shield. Bend the coil terminals over in an L shape to solder to the PC wiring terminal. Double check continuity once again. Scrape out excess solder between the terminals. Winding your own coils may take a little patience, but it's fun to do.

Layout out the PC board

Lay out the PCB as shown in Fig. 8-10. Variable capacitors C1 and C6 are mounted at the extreme outside. The RF and VFO coils (T1 and T2) are mounted alongside the respective capacitors. All parts are mounted on the top side of the PCB, with the PC wiring and a copper shield on the bottom side.

Cut a 2¼- ×–5-inch piece of double-sided PCB. Center and drill all holes for the variable capacitors before etching the board. These capacitors take up little room, but they should be mounted without crowding the other parts. IC1 is mounted on the bottom corner of the PCB (when viewing the PCB from the bottom). VFO coil (T2) is a tapped, shielded coil and is mounted close to IC1. IC2 is mounted at the center of the PCB (Fig. 8-11).

After the PC wiring is laid out on one side of the board, mask

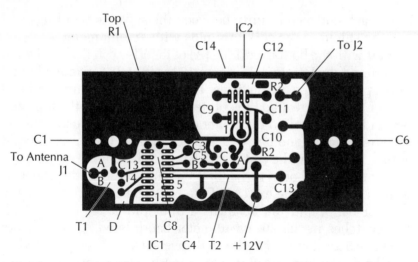

Fig. 8-10   *Notice both variable capacitors are mounted on a double-sided board with the other receiver components.*

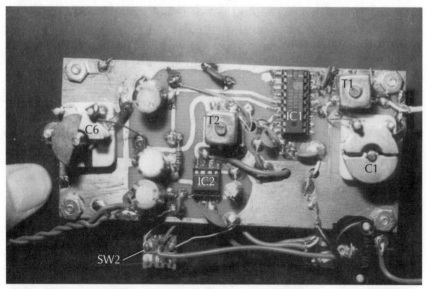

Fig. 8-11   *A close-up view of all the parts mounted on one side of the double-sided PCB.*

off the other side so the copper will remain. Place rubber plastic PVC tape over the blank side of the copper board. This copper side is used as a common shield and should be soldered to the ground side of the PC wiring.

Mounting parts

To mount parts, first mount both IC sockets. Bend all socket terminals flat. Use small-size solder to solder the terminals. Place each terminal over the correct area of PC wiring. Make a good solder connection. Pull a pocketknife blade between each terminal to clear out any rosin or excess solder. Double check each terminal from the top of the socket (plug-in side) to the PC wiring with an ohmmeter.

For small parts, be sure the component leads are as short as possible. Bend an L shape into the leads so they can be soldered against the PC wiring. Keep all leads away from each other so they do not short. Double check each wiring connection with a magnifying glass. Mount both coils after the other parts are mounted, except for the variable capacitors (Fig. 8-12).

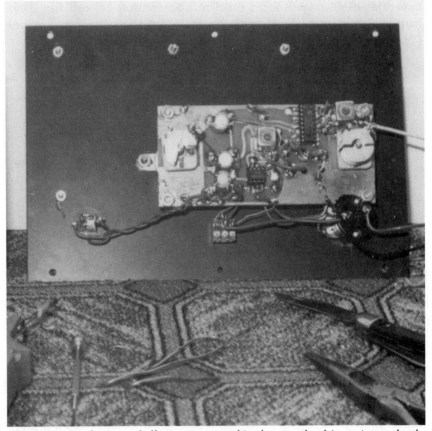

Fig. 8-12 *Back view of all parts mounted in the metal cabinet. A metal cabinet is used to prevent outside interference.*

Place a white dot on the PCB for terminal 1 of each IC socket, to indicate correct IC mounting. Check that all the pins of the ICs are in the socket instead of sticking out on the sides. Make sure IC1 is plugged in properly or you can ruin the IC within seconds. Also, do not short C6 to ground or IC1 is destroyed.

Drill a ⁵⁄₃₂-inch hole in each corner for mounting. Drill two ⅛-inch holes in the PCB for the shielded volume control leads. Drill one ⁵⁄₃₂-inch hole next to T2 for the B+ voltage and small switch wires.

Building the cabinet

Lay out the front panel as shown in Fig. 8-13. Drill ¹⁵⁄₆₄-inch holes for the headphone jack and for the toggle switch. Drill a ¼-inch hole for the capacitor (C1) extension shaft. Use several ⁵⁄₃₂-inch bit holes to make the large ¾-inch hole for mounting the reduction gear assembly. Round out the hole with a rat-tail file. Drill four ⁵⁄₃₂-inch holes to mount the PC chassis to the front panel. Choose a large metal chassis to mount the dial assembly.

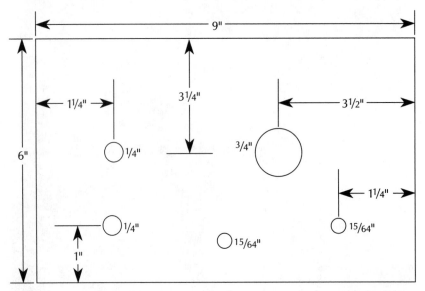

Fig. 8-13 *Layout of the front of the cabinet with required drill bit holes.*

Run a shielded wire from the antenna input from T1 to the antenna jack on the back cover. Use a shielded cable from and to volume control R1 to prevent hum and noise pick-up.

Adjusting the coils

Set both coil slugs even at the top outside shield. The VFO coil can be set with a frequency counter, another shortwave receiver, or a band locator. Set the dial pointer one-third of the way from the end of the dial. Place the band locator lead next to the VFO capacitor (C6). Rotate SW2 to the 20-meter (A–B) band. Adjust T2 out until WWV can be heard at 10 MHz in the headphones with the band locator set at 10 MHz. You should be able to hear WWV at 10 MHz with the band locator turned off. Mark the dial at 10 MHz.

Turn SW2 to the 40-meter band (A and C). Set the band adaptor at 7.35 MHz. Tune C6 until a 7.35 MHz signal can be heard from the adaptor. Mark the band on the dial assembly. The ham bands can be marked as they are tuned in. The 40 or 41-meter ham bands on CW (7 MHz–7.15 MHz), and CW and SSB (7.15 MHz–7.3 MHz) can be heard with coil A–C switched in. The 20-meter ham bands on CW (14 MHz–14.2 MHz) and SSB (14.2 MHz–14.3 MHz) can be heard with coil A–B switched in. Of course, international broadcast stations on 49, 41, 31, and 25 meters can also be heard between the two bands.

Adjust T2 (VFO) only once as the other bands can be heard when you switch the coil with SW2. Adjust T1 for a maximum signal in the middle of either band. T1 adjustment is not critical.

C1 can be eliminated, if desired, to cut down on the expense of the shortwave receiver. The broadband coil (T1) can be left untuned if you do not use C1.

Making a deluxe dial assembly

To add a little class to the shortwave receiver, why not use a 7:1 or 6:1 reduction gear assembly using a homemade dial. See Chapter 9 for the dial layout. Copy it from the book on paper. With a plastic laminated sheet over the paper dial, mount the template over the whole assembly.

Cut a 3¾-×–6-inch double-sided copper board. Mark off a ½-inch frame. To cut out the center section, drill five small ⁵⁄₃₂-inch bit holes in each corner for the hacksaw or saber saw blade. Keep the saw blade ¹⁄₁₆ inch away from the inside outline (Fig. 8-14).

Carefully cut out each section of the board. Then place the inside edge of the etched board in a bench vise. Smooth down all edges with a large file. Make the edges straight. Use the top edge of the vise as a guide. Place a small piece of wood or scrap board against the copper area so it will not be marred in the process.

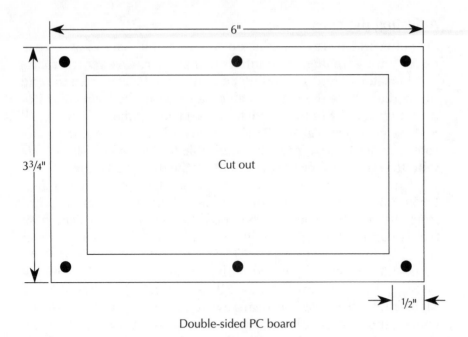

Double-sided PC board

Fig. 8-14 *Cut out the inside of a double-sided board to make a deluxe dial assembly panel plate.*

Sand down all edges with an electric bench sander, if handy. File off the outside and inside rough edges. Drill out 6 holes with a $\frac{5}{32}$-inch bit to hold the panel in place. If you do not want the bolt heads to show, grind down the bolt head to a flat surface. Solder the bolt to the back side of the PCB.

The template can be left with a copper or silver finish. To make a silver finish, use Tinnit™, which can be purchased at Digi-Key Corporation or most mail-order electronic stores. The material is supplied as a dry mixture with an indefinite shelf life. When mixed with water, the solution has a life of approximately six months.

Clean up the copper side with steel wool, soap, and water. Make sure all dirty marks, pencil, and finger prints are cleaned off. It's best to drill all holes before attempting to coat the copper surface. Follow the directions given with the Tinnit™ product. Wash off any chemical with household ammonia and water. Polish with a stainless steel cleaner and paper towel.

Place the panel on the front of the radio panel, and mark the holes to be drilled. Cut out the paper dial and cement it into position. The dial assembly goes over the reduction gear assembly. Place a plastic sheet over the dial assembly. Cut the laminated plastic ¼-inch wider than the dial area. The copper or silver template can be bolted over the entire dial assembly.

Cut out a piece of clear plastic to form the dial pointer. Drill small holes to fit on the reduction gear assembly. Fasten the pointer assembly to the reduction gear assembly. Place a large knob on the reduction gear shaft. Now you have a nice commercial-looking dial assembly like back in the early days of radio building (Fig. 8-15). This dial assembly can be mounted on other SW radio receivers.

Fig. 8-15 *Closeup of the deluxe dial assembly.*

Project 2: Varactor-tuning, direct-conversion receiver

What you will need

IC1	TDA7000 Signetics 18-pin IC chip (DC. Electronics)
IC2	LM386 audio output amp
L1	RF coil, 6 turns of #26 enameled wire (see text)
L2	RF coil, 46 turns of #26 enameled wire

L3	VFO coil, 46 turns of #26 enameled wire over a toroid T-50-2 coil form, tapped at the 10th and 24th turns.
C1, C4, C6, C12 & C13	0.1-μF, 50-volt NP0 (Negative-positive-zero) ceramic capacitor
C2, C9	0.001-μF, 50-volt NP0 capacitor
C3	0.002-μF, 50-volt NP0 capacitor
C5	10-μF, 35-volt electrolytic capacitor
C7, C10 & C11	220-μF, 35-volt electrolytic capacitor
C8	0.05-μF, 50-volt ceramic capacitor
R1	10-kilohm audio taper volume control with SPST switch
R2	10-ohm, ½-watt resistor
R3	100-ohm, ½-watt resistor
R4	4.7-kilohm, ½-watt resistor
R5	10-kilohm linear taper control
R6	1-kilohm, linear taper control
R7	100-kilohm, ¼-watt
TD1	MV2115 100-pF tuning (varactor) diode (Circuit Specialist or DC Electronics)
SW1	Single pole, single throw (SPST) switch on rear of R1
SW2	3-position rotary switch (Radio Shack, 275-1385 or equiv.)
Dip sockets	One 18-pin socket for IC1 and one 8-pin socket for IC2
J1, J2	Metal panel mount (Radio Shack, 274-346)
Cabinet	4 × 6 × 3-inch metal enclosure (LMB Cabinet 463N or TEN-TEC, TG36 or Hosfelt Electronics)
Vernier dial assembly	(Oak Hill Research, BD02 or Ocean State Electronics, VD112-10)
Misc.	Double-sided PCB, hookup wire, solder etc.

This shortwave receiver uses varactor tuning to cover the shortwave band from 7 MHz to 15 MHz. No variable capacitors are found in this circuit, making this SW receiver less costly to build. All coils are hand wound on T-50-2 toroid coil forms. These toroid forms are ½ inch in diameter, and red in color. They can be purchased in about every electronic supply store (Fig. 8-16).

Fig. 8-16   *This direct-conversion receiver is tuned with a varactor diode and hand-wound toroid coils.*

How the circuit works

A TDA7000 IC is used as the RF, mixer, and VFO oscillator circuits (Fig. 8-17). A balanced, untuned RF circuit does not have a variable capacitor or varactor tuning. L1 and L2 pick up the signal from the RF antenna, and feed it to terminals 13 and 14 of IC1.

The VFO coil (L3) is wound on another toroid form and has two taps, providing three different coils that can be switched into the VFO circuit. Varactor diode TD1 tunes each switched-in coil with a different dc voltage applied to the collector terminal. The diode is tied to the B+ circuit with ceramic bypass capacitor C9. R5 acts as a tuning adjustment, with R6 as a fine tuning or bandspread tuning adjustment.

When a different voltage is applied to TD1, the capacitance is changed, tuning in the SW band. However, since these small var-

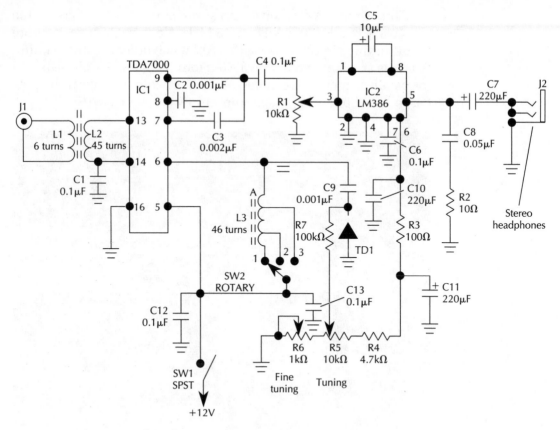

Fig. 8-17 *The schematic diagram of the simple direct-conversion receiver.*

actor diodes are limited in capacitance, it will not cover the whole band. By using several coils, each band can be covered.

By beating the incoming signal to the VFO tuned signal, you hear single sideband (SSB) and CW bands. Although the tuning is very delicate, good reception can be achieved. AM international broadcast stations need to be sharply tuned in between the loud whistling signals. Place a vernier dial or reduction gear on the end of R6 for sharper, easier tuning.

The audio signal is taken from pin 9 of IC1. C4 couples the audio signal to volume control R1. IC2 provides plenty of audio output to drive a small speaker or low-impedance headphones. Listening with headphones is best due to all the whistling and the CW signals.

Laying out the chassis

Cut a 2½-×-3½-inch piece of double-sided PCB from a larger piece. Lay out the PC wiring on one side, as shown in Fig. 8-18.

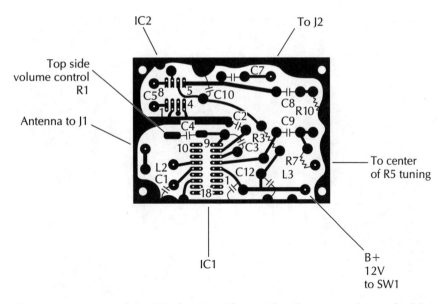

Fig. 8-18 *Layout of the PC chassis with toroid coils mounted on a double-sided board.*

The untuned RF coil is mounted on one side of IC1 and L3 is mounted on the other. The audio chip (IC2) is mounted above IC1 with a common shield between them. Cover the back of the double-sided board with tape so the copper side acts as a shield.

After all pads and wiring strips are laid out, start to etch the PCB. If you rock the board in the etching solution, the board should be etched in one half hour. Do not over etch. Check on the progress so as not to damage the fine PC wiring. Check continuity on each long strip of PC wiring with an ohmmeter to be sure there aren't any cracks. Drill out a $\frac{5}{32}$-inch mounting hole in each corner for mounting.

Mounting parts

Mount all small parts on the PCB. First mount both IC1 and IC2 DIP sockets. Spread out the pins on each socket so that they will lay flat and solder to each small pin. All parts are surface mounted since the other side of the copper is used as a shield. Bend a small L terminal on the end of each component before soldering it to the PCB (Fig. 8-19). Check each IC lead from the PC wiring to the top of the IC socket with the low-ohm scale of an ohmmeter. Pull a knife blade or screwdriver blade between each IC terminal to remove any excess solder or rosin.

Next mount all the small capacitors and resistors. Solder in

Fig. 8-19 *Closeup view of the parts mounted on the small PCB.*

Fig. 8-20 *Closeup view of L3 fastened to the board with rubber silicone cement.*

the larger electrolytic capacitors and double check that they have correct polarity. Mount both toroid coil forms last. Place a dab of rubber silicone cement or epoxy at the bottom of the coil if it moves around (Fig. 8-20).

Winding the coils

Cut off 2½ feet of #26 enameled wire for the RF coil (L2). Leave a 1-inch lead on the starting end. Wind on a total of 46 turns of wire for L2. Keep the wire taut and free from kinks. If one wire is wound over another coil wire, remove it and rewind it again. After L2 is completely wound, you should have a gap on the T-50-2 toroid form between the start and finish of the coil of ³⁄₁₆ inch (Fig. 8-21).

Wind on 6 turns of the same wire for L1, which is wound over the middle of L2. Try to keep the primary winding uniform

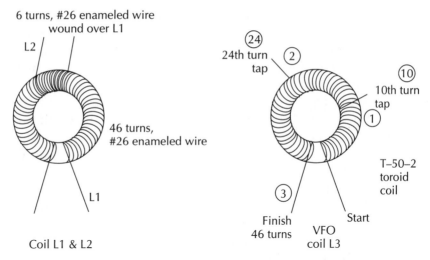

Fig. 8-21 *L1, L2, and L3 are wound with #26 enameled wire.*

and close together. When the coil wire goes through the middle of the toroid form that counts as one turn. Leave about 1 inch of coil at the end for board connections.

Now wind the VFO coil (L3) on another T-50-2 toroid form. This coil is 46 turns with a tap at the tenth and twenty-fourth turn. Make the taps on the middle, outside edge of the coil form. Twist each tap five or six times until they are about ¼-inch long.

Remove any kinks in the wire as it is threaded through the toroid hole. Pull kinked wire over a pencil or pen to straighten. Keep the wire taut while winding the coil so the wire does not unwind (Fig. 8-22).

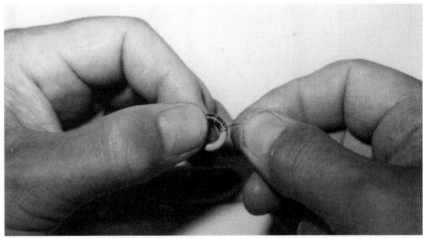

Fig. 8-22 *Winding the toroid coils with #26 enameled wire.*

When mounting coils, cut the leads as short as possible. Tin each wire lead by scraping off the enamel coating, or you can use a very hot soldering iron to melt it off. Make sure the lead is clean, and is covered with solder when you are done. Likewise, make a good, clean connection at each coil tap. Check each tap for continuity with an ohmmeter.

The top of the coil (A) with the first tap (after the tenth turn) is common, and connects to terminal 6 of IC1. Run a direct lead to the rotary-type switch. Keep all leads as short as possible. The last coil end (D) is switched in last.

Three different bands tune in the ham bands on 40 meters with CW from 7 MHz to 7.1 MHz, and 7.1 MHz to 7.3 MHz for sideband operation. The 20-meter CW ham signals are found at 14 MHz to 14.2 MHz, and sideband (SSB) is at 14.2 MHz to 14.3 MHz. Use R6 (1K) to fine tune the sidebands.

Laying out the cabinet

Drill all holes as shown in Fig. 8-23. Tape a piece of paper over the front area with the required holes shown to prevent scratching the front panel. It's best to drill a small hole first, and then enlarge it with the correct size bit when drilling out the thin metal panel. Enlarge the vernier dial assembly hole to ¾ inch.

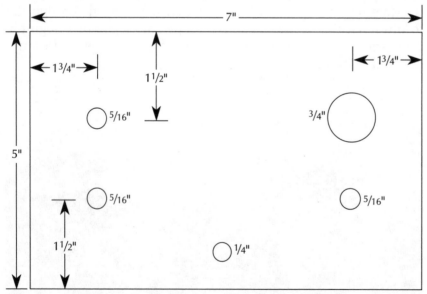

Fig. 8-23 *Follow this front panel layout diagram, to position the drill bit holes.*

The tuning control (R5) is mounted behind the front panel on a bracket so the vernier dial assembly will lay flat. R1, R6 and SW2 are mounted directly on the front panel. The PCB chassis is bolted to the front chassis close to SW2. Mount J1 on the rear chassis panel.

Keep all leads as short as possible when connecting outside parts to the PCB chassis. Use small shielded cable to run to the antenna jack (J1), and to and from the volume control (R1) to prevent noise or interference. Double check all connections before wiring up the receiver.

Troubleshooting

Make sure both IC1 and IC2 are properly set in their DIP sockets. Check for any pins that may have not made it in the socket when installing IC1. If IC1 is installed backwards, or pin 6 is accidentally shorted to chassis ground, the IC1 is ruined immediately.

Connect a low-impedance pair of headphones to J2, and the outside antenna to J1. Switch on the receiver and turn the volume half way up. Rotate the vernier dial to locate stations. Single sideband (SSB) ham stations and international broadcast stations are difficult to tune in, while CW is rather easy. Use R6 as a bandspreading tuning control.

If no sound is heard, rotate the volume control back and forth and you should hear some hum. Place the blade of a screwdriver on the center terminal of the volume control. A loud click or hum indicates the audio circuit is okay. Check voltage on pins 5, 6, 1 and 8 of IC2 if there is no sound. Double check the seating of IC2. A total current reading should be around 16.9 mA (Fig. 8-24).

When hum is heard at the volume control, but no stations come in, go to IC2. Check voltages on pin 5 and 6. Check terminals 6 and 13 with a small screwdriver blade. You should hear a loud click. Do not short the screwdriver to ground while on any terminals. If the voltage reading is good, but no stations can be tuned in, suspect a defective IC1. Replace it.

Make an angle bracket to support the tuning control (R5), from a piece of aluminum or light metal. If need be, the dial assembly screws that hold the variable tuning control shaft can be removed to mount the dial assembly. Replace the screws after the dial assembly is mounted. The bottom two dial assembly mounting bolts can be used to hold the metal bracket in position.

This direct-conversion receiver can be powered from eight AA nickel-cadmium batteries. These batteries can be recharged

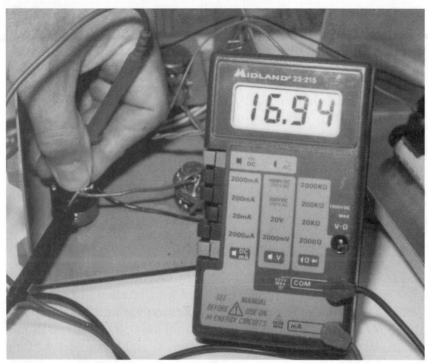

Fig. 8-24 *Normal current drain of the circuit without a station tuned in, and with the volume turned down.*

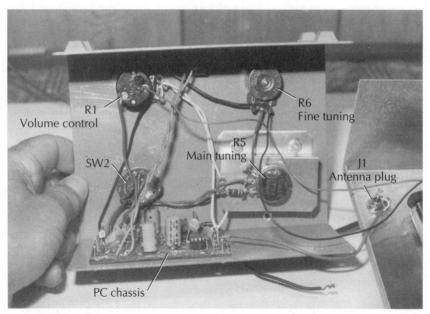

Fig. 8-25 *Back view of the completed direct-conversion receiver.*

overnight when they run down. Select two different AA battery holders and wire them in series to supply a 12-volt source.

This direct-conversion receiver is fairly cheap to build since it doesn't use any large variable capacitors (Fig. 8-25). Not only is it cheap, but fun too! If only one band is needed, leave off SW2 and use all of L3 without any taps to receive the 40-meter band. Happy listening!

Project 3: Shortwave superhet receiver

What you will need

IC1	TDA7000-RF-oscillator-mixer (DC Electronics)
IC2	LM386 audio output IC
Q1, Q2	2N3904 universal transistor
TD1	100-pF varactor diode MV2115 (DC Electronics)
D1	1N34 or 1N270 diode
L1	6 turns, #26 enameled wire, wound over L2
L2	49 turns, #26 enameled wire
L3	54 turns, #26 enameled wire. All coils are wound in T-50-2 toroid forms (see text)
C1, C4, C6, C8, C18	0.01-µF, 50-volt ceramic capacitor
C2, C5, C7, C9, C10, C13, C15	0.1-µF, 50-volt ceramic capacitor
C3	0.001-µF, 50-volt monolytic capacitor or 5% ceramic capacitor
C11, C12, & C17	220-µF, 35-volt electrolytic capacitor
C14	100-µF, 35-volt electrolytic capacitor
C16	0.05-µF, 50-volt ceramic capacitor
C19	10-µF, 35-volt electrolytic capacitor
CF1	455 kHz ceramic filter network (Digi-key Corp, TK2331 or DC Electronics, CFU455DF

R1, R9 & R10	3.3-kilohm, ¼-watt resistors
R2, R6	47-kilohm, ¼-watt resistors
R3	100-ohm, ¼-watt resistors
R4	220-ohm, ¼-watt resistors
R5, R11	2.2-kilohm ¼-watt resistors
R7	5.6- kilohm, ¼-watt resistors
R8	470-ohm, ¼-watt resistors
R12	4.7-kilohm, ¼-watt resistor
R13	10-kilohm linear control
R14	1-kilohm linear control
R15	100-ohm, ¼-watt resistor
R16	10-kilohm audio taper control with SPST switch on rear
R17	10-ohm, ¼-watt resistor
R18	100-kilohm, ¼-watt resistor
J1	Panel mount jack (Radio Shack, 274-346)
J2	³⁄₃₂-inch headphone jack (Radio Shack, 274-247 For speaker & head phone, Radio Shack, 274-292)
Vernier dial assembly	45K N100 (DC Electronics)
Cabinet	5-×–6-×–4-inch plain aluminum LMB metal cabinet or equiv. (DC Electronics, 564N)
Misc.	Knobs, bolts & nuts, solder, hookup wire, double-sided PCB, 18-pin and 8-pin IC DIP sockets, etc.

This shortwave receiver uses a 455-kHz superhet IF circuit with varactor-tuned toroid coils. The receiver covers the 20, 30, and 40-meter band. You can use a small 4-inch permanent magnet (PM) speaker with this receiver, although headphones should be used on the ham SSB, and CW bands. The VFO circuit tunes from 7.25-MHz to 20.5-MHz frequencies using a tapped coil (Fig. 8-26).

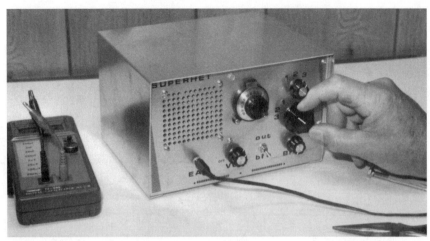

Fig. 8-26   *This shortwave receiver uses a superhet circuit with varactor tuning, toroid wound coils, and a 455-kHz ceramic filter network.*

How the circuit works

RF signal is fed from the outside antenna to J1, and to L1 (Fig. 8-27). Coil L2 couples the RF signal to an untuned front end at terminals 13 and 14 of IC1. Pin 6 of the TDA7000 chip has a tapped toroid coil (L3, VFO) to tune in the various frequencies. L3 is tuned with low-priced varactor diode TD1 (100 pF). C3 isolates TD1 from the B+ voltage at the top of the coil.

Although most varactor diodes have a short tuning range, TD1 tunes signals across the entire rotation of linear resistor R13. R13 is the basic tuner, applying a varying dc voltage to the top of the varactor diode (TD1). R14 acts as a vernier tuner, separating the stations. This 1-k resistor does a fine job of pinpointing and separating ham stations on CW or SSB bands.

The mixed RF signal is coupled to the ceramic 455-kHz IF filter (CF1), and to the resistance/capacitance coupled IF stages. Q1 and Q2 amplify the weak 455-kHz intermediate frequency (IF) to C8. The 0.01-μF capacitor couples the IF frequency which is rectified by diode D1 (1N34).

The audio signal is controlled by volume control R16. The audio input signal is applied to pin 3 of IC2. If a speaker is to be used all the time, insert a transistor audio stage between the volume control and IC2. IC2 in the present circuit will drive a small PM speaker with adequate audio on stronger shortwave stations.

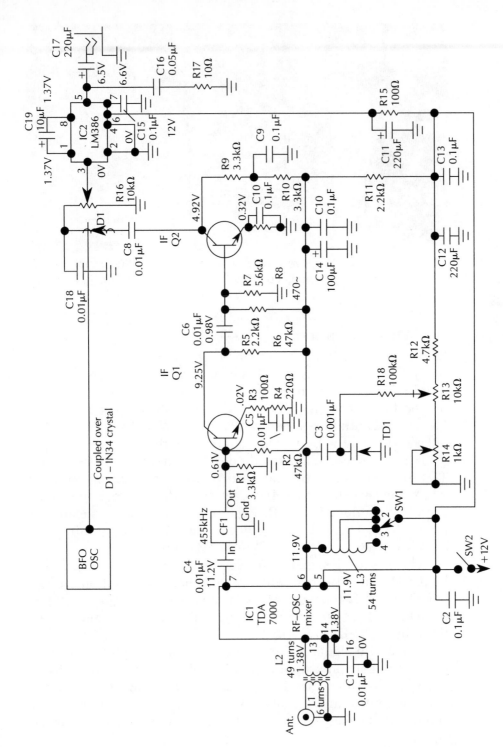

Fig. 8-27 *L1 and L2 couple the input RF signal to chip IC1, and the signal's tuned with a varactor diode and L3 in a VFO circuit.*

Winding the coils

Both sets of coils are wound on T-50-2 (½-inch) toroid forms. These forms are usually red in color. Wind on a total of 49 turns for L2. Keep the wires tightly together at the center area of the form. Then wind on 6 turns of #26 enameled wire for L1 over the center of L2. These coils are self-supporting when the leads are cut short and soldered to the correct terminals. Solder L2 to terminals 13 and 14 of IC1. One side of L1 is soldered to ground, and the other side to J1.

Wind on a total of 54 turns for L3 on another T-50-2 toroid form. Tap each coil winding as shown in Fig. 8-28. Simply fold over the wire on the outside edge, and twist 6 turns. Then continue winding the wire for the next switch terminal. Do not cut the coil wire until the winding is finished. Leave ½ inch of wire from the coil form on the 54th turn.

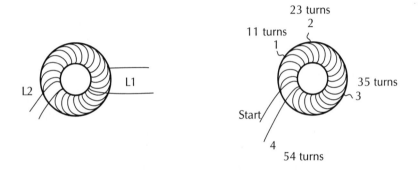

L1—6 turns, #26 enameled wire

L2—49 turns, #26 enameled wire

L3—54 turns, #26 enameled wire tapped at the 11th turn, 23rd turn, 35th turn and at the finish, 54th turn.

Fig. 8-28 *L1, L2 and L3 are wound on a T-50-2 Toroid coil form.*

Scrape off the enamel coating from the ends of the wire and from the coil taps for a good solder connection. Tin each end before mounting the coil. The four coil taps are located at the 11th, 23rd, the 35th, and the 54th turn.

Solder the beginning of the coil winding to the PC wiring of terminal 6. Cement L3 to the PCB with silicone rubber cement.

Connect an extension wire to the other leads that go to SW1. Cement all wires to the PCB before the board is mounted inside the metal cabinet (Fig. 8-29).

Fig. 8-29 *A closeup view of the PCB with external connecting parts.*

Laying out the cabinet

Choose a cabinet large enough to hold a front-mounted speaker. The volume control, fine tuning control, varactor tuning knob, switch SW1, and headphone jack are mounted on the front panel. Remember to mount the vernier dial assembly for easy tuning. R13 was mounted on a separate bracket attached to the dial assembly mounting bolts.

Lay out the front dial components on a sheet of paper. Tape the paper to the front of the cabinet to line up the holes exactly, and to prevent scratching the cabinet. Remove the paper after all the holes are drilled (Fig. 8-30).

Mount the PCB chassis close to the front panel with a bolt in each corner. The coil leads should be as close to SW1 as possible. Use plastic or metal spacers to hold the chassis rigid. Connect the shielded cable to the antenna jack (J1) and to the volume control circuits.

Laying out the PC board

Cut a 3-×–4½-inch piece of double-sided copper board from a larger piece. Lay out the pads and wiring on the board as shown in Fig. 8-31. Keep IC1 close to the bottom of the PCB to make room for the other parts. The 18-pin DIP socket is mounted in a

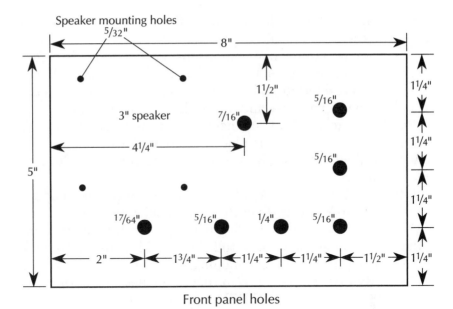

Fig. 8-30   *Correct layout of front panel holes in the metal cabinet. Using a metal cabinet helps block strong local FM and broadcast stations.*

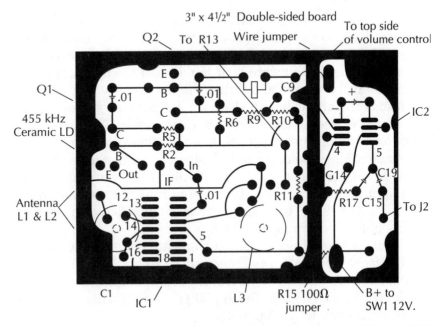

Fig. 8-31   *Layout of the PCB wiring with audio circuit to the right, and RF circuits in a grounded square.*

frame of copper wiring. The RF and VFO circuits are isolated by copper ground from the audio circuits.

There are two jumper connections that need to be made before mounting any components. Run an insulated wire from D1 to the audio input board terminal. Resistor R15 (100 ohm) straddles the ground wiring between B+ and decoupling capacitor C11.

Remember to make all connecting wire flat against the PC wiring. A separate B+ lead is placed between the switch and the 12-volt terminal. R15 provides isolation between the audio and RF circuits.

Cover the back of the PCB before etching so that the copper foil remains on. You can cover the entire back with Radio Shack PVC electrical tape (64-2349). Just overlap each ¾-inch strip until the entire copper side is covered. After etching the PCB, check that no wiring is too close or touching, causing a short.

Carefully inspect the board for poorly etched or intermittent wiring. Double check the IC DIP socket connections to be sure none of the leads are touching. Cut between the copper wiring with a razor blade or pocketknife. Several cuts may be needed. Look over the entire board with a magnifying glass.

Mounting parts

Keep all component ground leads inside the copper shielded area. Solder in both IC sockets after the jumpers are made. Make sure each socket terminal fits over the wiring where it is to be mounted. When IC pins are bent flat against the board, the connections must be made wider than are necessary when you feed the leads through the board. Use a small tip on the soldering iron with small diameter solder for the IC terminals. This helps prevent excess solder from spreading to the other pin terminals.

As mentioned before, run the edge of a pocketknife or small screwdriver blade between each IC pin to be sure there is no overlapping solder or rosin. Check continuity between each pin and the PC wiring. Then check the resistance between the pins for possible overlapping of solder.

Mount all small resistors and capacitors after the IC sockets are in place. Mount the small ceramic 455-kHz (CF1) filter component. Be sure to observe correct input and output connections. Solder L1, L2 and L3 last. Secure L3 (VFO coil) with rubber silicone cement or epoxy (Fig. 8-32).

Next solder all components on the audio section of the circuit. Bend a small L at the connecting terminals for easy soldering. Connect a small shielded cable onto the audio input and

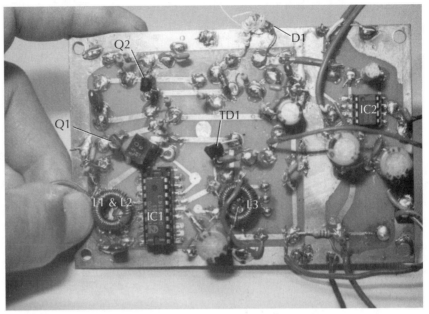

Fig. 8-32 *A closeup view of the PCB with parts soldered into position.*

from the output going to volume control (R16). Use a red flexible wire to the switch SW2. Solder a ground and audio output wire to the headphone jack or speaker (J2).

When mounting diodes and electrolytic capacitors, check that you have observed correct polarity (Fig. 8-33). Make sure each transistor terminal is correctly placed. Improper placement of IC, transistor, or ceramic filter (455 kHz) terminals may prevent the receiver from operating.

SSB tuning

Because the receiver is a superhet, the ham single sidebands (SSB) will sound garbled when tuned in. This is just the opposite of the direct-conversion SW receiver. In direct-conversion, the amateur and CW signals are beat against the VFO signal to erase the garbled sound. Here a separate beat-frequency oscillator (BFO) must beat against the 455-kHz signal at the crystal detector to clear up the garbled audio. Of course, some ham operators on 40 meters operate on AM and therefore have a normal voice.

The BFO unit uses a 455-kHz IF transformer (Fig. 8-34). You can change the 455-kHz frequency with a small 10-pF variable capacitor or resistor. SW3 turns on the BFO unit when ham signals are located. Rotate the control to change the sound of the voice until it is clear and distinct. Sometimes this tuning is

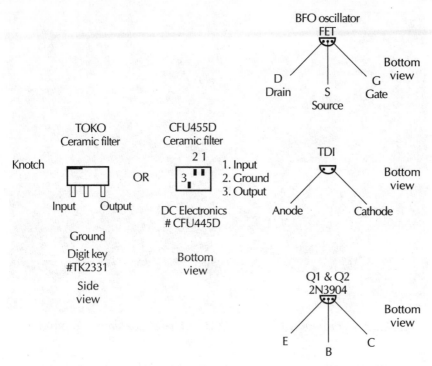

Fig. 8-33   *The correct connections for CF1, Q1 and Q2 and TD1.*

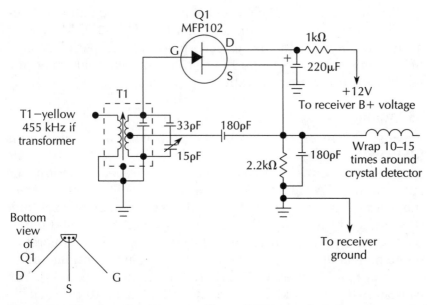

Fig. 8-34   *The beat-frequency oscillator (BFO) circuit is loosely coupled around the detector (1N34).*

hard to do because of too many signals on top of one another. Adjust the vernier control and the BFO control to separate the voice for SSB operation.

Set the frequency of the 455-kHz transformer with a signal generator or frequency counter. Mark the setting on top of the can with pen or pencil. Tune in a strong ham station, and rotate the control to clear up the voice. When a variable capacitor is used for tuning, mesh all the capacitor plates, and barely touch the 455-kHz adjustment until the voice is clear. Likewise, on a variable resistor control, set the control in the middle of its rotation for the adjustment.

To connect the SSB unit to the shortwave receiver circuit, wrap about 12 turns of coil wire around the glass area of a 1N34 diode, and bring the lead out. Do not connect the wire directly to the circuit. Tape the coil wire to the diode so it will not come loose. Run wire to the BFO unit on the front panel. Shut off the BFO when listening to foreign or American broadcast stations.

Testing the circuit

It's best to test out the small SW receiver when the PCB is completed but not yet installed in the cabinet. You can find and change a defective part if the receiver does not function. Double check all wiring before turning on the receiver. Solder a short wire from +12 volts to the 54th turn of coil L3. This is only temporary, and is used as SW1 to check out the receiver. Make sure both ICs are correctly mounted.

With the volume control wide open and SW2 turned on, you should hear some type of noise or stations. Rotate tuning control R13. Stations should be heard all over the band. Check the voltage on pin 6 of IC2 and pins 5 and 6 of IC1 if the receiver is dead. Suspect a bad SW2, faulty leads, or a bad battery. Take a current measurement across the switch terminals (19.5 mA). Excessive current may indicate a leaky IC, improper polarity of the electrolytic capacitors, or shorted PC wiring.

Touch the top of the volume control and listen for a loud hum. If you hear a hum, you can assume the audio stages are normal. If no hum is heard in the speaker or headphones, this may indicate a broken connection or component. Check the voltages of each pin of IC2 and compare it with the schematic. Carefully check all the audio wiring (Fig. 8-35).

Because the IF stage uses a fixed ceramic 455-kHz filter network, no IF adjustment is needed. Only the SSB adaptor (455

Fig. 8-35 *Back view of the wired-up receiver before placing on the top cover.*

kHz) must be adjusted when the ham band is located. This adaptor can be eliminated if you do not desire to listen to the ham bands. There are a lot of other stations to tune in with this superhet receiver.

Reducing interference

You might find strong shortwave, broadcast, or FM stations creeping into the shortwave bands. Placing the shortwave receiver inside a tight metal case helps. But strong local FM stations might still come in on bands 3 and 4. A small interference trap eliminates most of the radiated signals and is easy to build.

The trap circuit can be placed on a small perfboard and connected between the antenna jack (J1) and L1. The homemade toroid coil can be wound on a small T-50-2 or T-37-2 toroid form. Wind on 22 turns of #24 enameled wire for coil L1.

Coil L1 and C1 are tied to common ground. C1 can be a small variable or trimmer capacitor. All capacitors are silver mica types. Wire the interference trap circuit as shown in Fig. 8-36. Keep all leads as short as possible. After the circuit is wired, adjust C1 until the FM station is at its weakest signal (about mid range). Replace the metal cabinet cover.

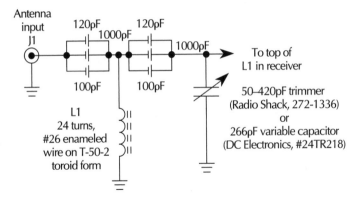

Fig. 8-36 *Build this interference trap to help block strong shortwave, broadcast, and FM stations from coming in on the shortwave bands.*

Hooking up the speaker

By using a closed-circuit phone jack (Radio Shack, 274-246), the speaker is on when the headphones are unplugged. Likewise, when the headphones are inserted, the speaker is disconnected from the circuit (Fig. 8-37). The three-conductor (stereo) jack has 5 different terminals. Connect terminals 2 and 5 together for the headphones and terminals 3 and 4 together for the speaker. Solder the audio wire from the output capacitor to pins 2 and 5.

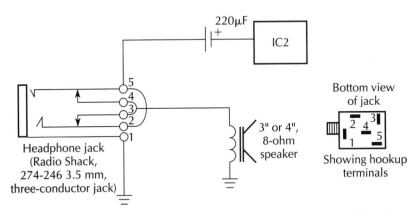

Fig. 8-37 *Wire the speaker into the circuit with a close-circuit jack. The audio output connects to headphone jacks on terminals 2 & 5.*

❖9

Construction notes and where to find parts

THIS CHAPTER TELLS YOU HOW TO MAKE YOUR OWN DIALS, DIAL pointers and reduction gear pointers. All solid-state devices, including transistors, ICs, and varactor tuning diode connections are also described here, as well as tube socket connections. At the end of this chapter, you will also find a section telling you where to obtain all the parts found in the various receiver projects in this book.

Making your own dial decals

You can make your own dials for variable capacitors, switches, and volume controls from the drawings found in Figs. 9-1, 9-2,

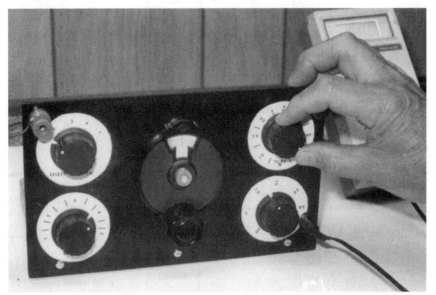

Fig. 9-1 *Make your own dial assemblies out of paper, laminated plastic, and rub-on letters and numbers.*

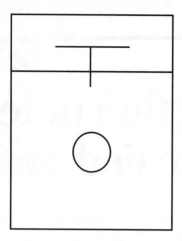

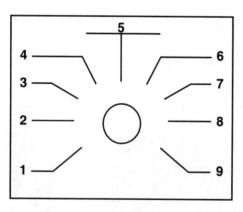

Fig. 9-2 *Volume controls and switch decals can be copied and cemented to the front panel with a laminated plastic cover.*

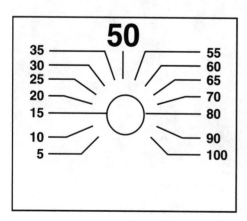

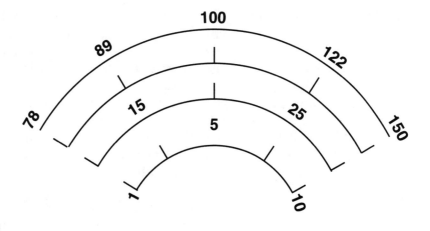

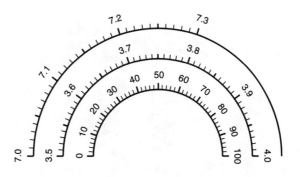

Fig. 9-3 *Copy the tuning dial assembly that will fit on the front panel of your shortwave radio.*

and 9-3. Just make a copy of the dial that you need to place on the front panel of the receivers you decide to build. The decals can be cemented to the front panel with model or plastic cement. Then cover the white dial assembly with stick-on laminating sheets found at stationery or art stores.

Cut the laminated clear plastic sheet ¼-inch larger than the dial assembly. Cut out the center hole so it will fit under the mounting nut. Cement the dial assembly in the correct position by applying the adhesive side and pressing firmly. Be sure to remove any bubbles. You can apply laminated sheets on both sides of the cut-out dial assembly and cement them to the front panel.

Rub-on project labels and dial assemblies can be purchased from Radio Shack (270-201), Digi-Key, and other electronic supply houses (Fig. 9-4). Simply rub on the decal and letters with a pencil lead or blunt object. Then spray clear lacquer or varnish over the dial assembly to protect the finish.

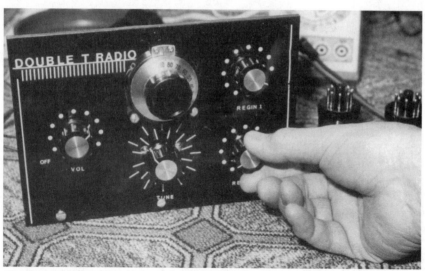

Fig. 9-4 *Rub-on labels, numbers, and letters can be obtained from many electronic local and mail-order firms. Check local hobby and craft stores for rub-on numbers.*

Making your own dial pointer

You can make your own dial assembly for that shortwave receiver using a variable capacitor and reduction gear. The capacitor has a larger shaft and hub than the reduction gear assembly. Choose a small plastic knob with set screw to hold the metal pointer. The shaft is just a little larger than the regular ¼-inch shaft.

First drill out the front of the plastic knob with a ¼-inch bit. Then select a larger bit to drill out the brass insert to fit over the hub area. Select a drill bit the same size as the capacitor shaft. Hold the plastic knob (wrap cloth around the knob) with a pair of pliers. Take only a small amount of brass off at a time. If needed, grind off thickness of knob to fit between outside knob.

After the large hole is drilled out, drill two small holes on each side of the pointer of the small black knob. A Radio Shack (274-415) knob was used here. Select a piece of copper solid wire (#12). Strip off the insulation of a short piece of #12 Romex cable wire. You can pick up a piece of this scrap wire from any electrical shop (Fig. 9-5).

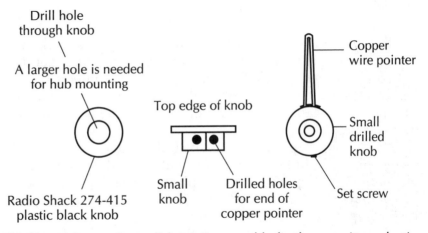

Drill hole through knob

A larger hole is needed for hub mounting

Top edge of knob

Copper wire pointer

Small drilled knob

Radio Shack 274-415 plastic black knob

Small knob

Drilled holes for end of copper pointer

Set screw

Fig. 9-5 *Make your own dial pointer assembly for the capacitor reduction drive with a plastic knob and #12 copper wire.*

Make sure the piece of copper wire you are going to use for the pointer is straight. Measure the length you will need the pointer to be to cover the entire dial assembly. Place a small nail in a vise, and bend it so that it is doubled. Apply extra pressure by placing the hair pin copper pointer in the metal vise. Cut the copper wire ends for the correct length.

You may have to bend the pointer ends to fit in the small knob holes. Pound the copper ends into the plastic holes. Place epoxy around the small holes and the copper wire. Let it set overnight. Now the pointer assembly can be mounted and tightened with a regular knob screw. You now have a professional looking dial pointer assembly (Fig. 9-6).

Fig. 9-6 *The professional appearance of a homemade vernier reduction-drive and dial assembly.*

To finish the dial numbers and lettering, select a 25-lb piece of paper or light cardboard. Draw or sketch the dial markings with a pencil first, then a felt pen. Use rub-on numbers and letters if you want to make it look really nice. Cement the paper dial into position. Mark the volume control and the headphone jack on the front panel.

Now cut out a piece of laminated plastic to go over the dial assemblies. Carefully measure the holes for the front components. Cut out round holes in the plastic sheet. Lay the piece of plastic over the dial area. Make sure the plastic covering is ¼-inch larger than the dial assembly.

Remove the paper back from the lamination, and center it over the controls. Line up the holes. Start at the center and work outward towards the ends. Remove all creases and bubbles. The plastic lamination not only keeps the dial assembly clean, but it protects the surface from wear and tear.

Making a reduction gear pointer

The reduction gear assembly helps slow down the rotation of the main tuning capacitor in the shortwave receiver. These reduction drives may have a 6:1, 10:1, or a 2:1 speed drive ratio. Always select the reduction gear assembly with a ¼-inch input and output for the shaft and knob (Fig. 9-7).

These reduction gear assemblies come without a dial assembly, so why not construct your own? Some outside shaft assemblies have two small mounting screws for mounting a plastic pointer.

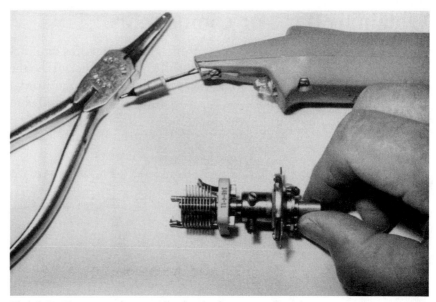

Fig. 9-7 *To properly tune in those shortwave bands, use a 6:1 or 10:1 reduction-drive assembly.*

Take a low-priced plastic ruler and cut it to length. Form a pointer at the end, or place a black line down the middle. Drill out the two small holes and the large hub hole at the front of the assembly.

Most reduction gear assemblies mount on the front panel. Make your own dial assembly as shown in this chapter. Select a large knob to go over the reduction gear assembly, and you have a professional looking reduction gear dial assembly (Fig. 9-8).

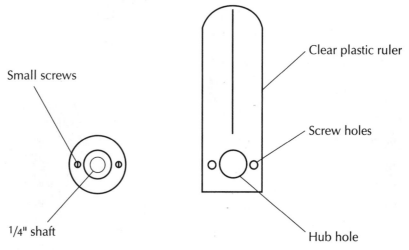

Fig. 9-8 *Bolt on a modified plastic ruler, and you have a professional-looking tuning pointer.*

Obtaining parts or components

Always, try to purchase parts locally from electronic stores or at Radio Shack. The more you can pick up locally, the quicker will be the construction process. If additional parts are needed, try mail-order firms (Fig. 9-9). Many transistors, ICs, resistors, capacitors, and controls can be purchased from your local radio/TV technician.

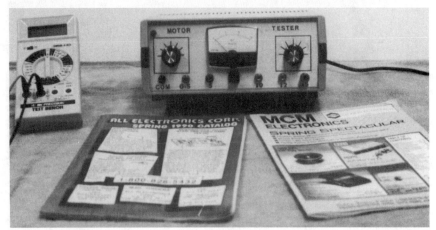

Fig. 9-9 *If electronic parts cannot be found locally, order them from mail-order firms.*

Fig. 9-10 *Do not forget that you can order electronic parts from radio surplus markets.*

If you decide to build several radio projects, order all parts from one or two different firms. This way you will be above the minimum order requirements and you will receive the components you need. Send for a catalog from various firms before ordering any parts. Sometimes the part numbers mentioned in the book may vary or they may change. Don't forget electronic firms in the surplus market (Fig. 9-10). Below are the various mail-order firms from which you can order electronic parts.

All Electric Corporation
P.O. Box 567
Van Nuys, CA 91408

American Design Corporation
815 Fairview Ave.
P.O. Box 220
Fairview, NJ 07022

Amiden Associates
P.O. Box 956
Torrance, CA 90508

Antique Electronic Supply
6221 S. Maple Ave.
Tempe, AZ 85283

BCD Electro
P.O. Box 830119
Richardson, TX 75083

Budget Electronics
P.O. Box 1477
Mareon Valley, CA 92337

Byers Chassis Kits
5120 Harmony Grove Rd.
Dover, PA 17315

Circuit Specialists
P.O. Box 3047
Scottsdale, Arizona 85271-3047

Consolidated Electronics
705 Waterviet Ave.
Dayton, OH 45420-2599

DC Electronics
P.O. Box 3203
Scottsdale, AZ 85271-3203

Digi-Key Corporation
701 Brooks Ave. So.
Box 677
Thief River Falls, MN 56701

Elenco Electronics Incorporated
150 W. Carpenter Ave.
Wheeling, IL 60090

Easy Tech Incorporated
2917 Bayview Dr.
Fremont, CA 94538

Fordham Radio
260 Motor Pkwy.
Hauppauge, NY 11788

Global Specialities
70 Fulton Terrace
New Haven, CT 06512

Hosfelt Electronics Incorporated
2700 Sunset Blvd.
Steubenville, OH 43952

H&R Company
18 Canal St.
P.O. Box 122
Bristol, PA 19007-0122

International Electronics
P.O. Box 170215
Arlington, TX 76003

Jameco Electronics
1355 Shoreway Rd.
Belmont, CA 94002

KA7QJY Components
Box 3893
Logan, UT 84323-3893

MCM Electronics
858 E. Congress Park Dr.
Centerville, OH 45459-4072

Micro Mart
508 Central Ave.
Westfield, NJ 07090

Mouser Electronics
National Circulation Center
P.O. Box 699
Mansfield, TX 76063

Ocean State Electronics
P.O. Box 1458
6 Industrial Dr.
Westerly, RI 02891

Oak Hill Research
20879 Madison St.
Big Rapids, MI 49307

Parts Express
390 E. First St.
Dayton, OH 45402

Project Pro
1710 Enterprise Pkwy.
Twinsburg, OH 44087

Radio Shack
1400 One Tandy Ln.
Fort Worth, TX 76102

Solid State Sales
P.O. Box 74D
Somerville, MA 02143

Transistor-IC-tube connections

The various transistor, IC, and tube-base connections are shown in Fig. 9-11. Notice this is the bottom view of the transistors and tubes. The top pin connections are given for IC components. These base connections are found in the different radio projects.

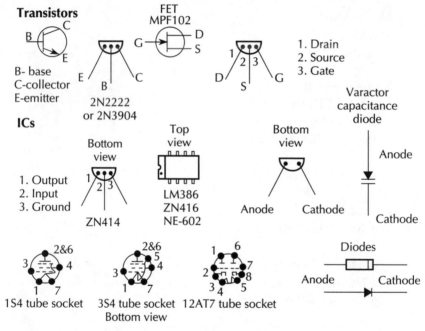

Fig. 9-11   *Transistor, IC, tube, and diode terminals and connections.*

Index

* **Boldface** numbers refer to art

* **Boldface** numbers refer to art

* **Boldface** numbers refer to art

* **Boldface** numbers refer to art